THE ILLUSTRATED GUIDE TO THE NIGHT SKY

THE ILLUSTRATED GUIDE TO THE NIGHT SKY

ROBIN KERROD

LONDON NEW YORK SYDNEY TORONTO

A QUARTO BOOK

This edition published 1993 by BCA
by arrangement with Quarto Publishing plc
CN 8141

This book was designed and produced by
Quarto Publishing plc

Senior Art Editor Mark Stevens
Designer John Strange
Star map plots Richard Monkhouse and John Cox; David Kemp
(hemispheres 44-67)
Illustrations Janos Marffy; Ron Jobson (moon maps 109-117)
Senior Editor Sally MacEachern
Copy Editor Eileen Cadman
Picture Research Manager Rebecca Horsewood
Art Director Moira Clinch
Publishing Director Janet Slingsby

With special thanks to Dr Ron Maddison, Astronaut
Memorial Planetarium and Observatory, Florida

Typeset by CST, Eastbourne
Manufactured in Singapore by Bright Arts Pte Ltd
Printed in Singapore by Star Standard Industries (Pte) Ltd

CONTENTS

INTRODUCTION

The night sky has fascinated people since before the dawn of civilization. The first recorded writings in the Middle East, in cuneiform and hieroglyphics some 5,000 years ago, bear witness to a thorough knowledge of the stars and constellations. But, by and large, the heavens remained mysterious and awesome.

Not until the early seventeenth century did the night sky begin to give up some of its secrets. That was when Galileo trained his telescope on the heavens, and spied moons circling Jupiter and phases of Venus. It was the beginning of an age of astronomical enlightenment that in turn saw Kepler explain the motion of the planets, Newton elaborate the phenomenon of gravity, and Herschel discover Uranus.

But it was not until Bessel determined the distance to a nearby star, 61 Cygni, that the enormity of the stellar Universe became apparent. Then, early this century, Hubble, using the newly completed 100-inch (254-centimetre) Hooker telescope, proved that spiral nebulae are separate island galaxies millions of light years away. The Universe began to assume dimensions beyond the grasp of the human mind.

In recent years radio astronomy and space astronomy by satellites and probes have brought to light an array of enigmatic bodies such as quasars and pulsars, bursters and blazars. It seems that the deeper we probe into the make-up of the Universe, the more complex it becomes, confirming J.B.S. Haldane's remark: "The Universe is not only queerer than we imagine, it is queerer than we can imagine".

The star-studded firmament has lost some of its former mystery and, because of increasing light pollution, some of its former brilliance. But, when you are away from city lights, look up and enjoy the night sky with eyes, binoculars and telescope. Travel in the mind's eye across interstellar space and ponder on the nature of the Universe and on the meaning of it all.

And may you have clear skies.

STRUCTURE OF THE BOOK

Designed and structured to be user-friendly, this guide introduces the night sky with little preamble. Would-be observers do not have to wade through pages of astronomical information before feasting their eyes on the magnificent heavens. Yet extra information is always instantly available, via the novel icon-based cross-referencing system.

In the main, the book is organized on a spread-by-spread basis, with each spread covering a particular aspect of the night sky or presenting reference information on a specific topic. Each chapter of the book follows a similar pattern. After an opening spread, a two-page introduction precedes spreads on the featured subject. The chapter closes with a number of reference spreads.

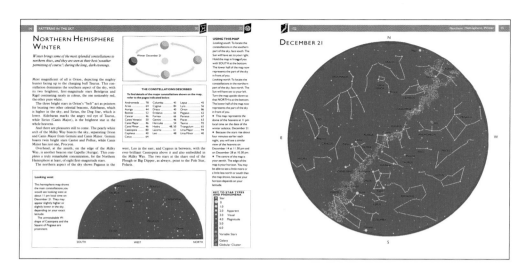

▲ Seasonal star maps

The main maps in Chapter 1 present the first level of information about the night sky. They help observers familiarize themselves with the constellations that come into view season by season. Half-circle sketch maps are included to help interpretation, showing examples of sky views in a particular direction.

▶ Monthly star maps

The main maps in Chapter 2 provide more detailed information about the stars and constellations visible month by month throughout the year. They feature the brightest nebulae, clusters and galaxies. Half-circle sketch maps are again included to help interpretation. They show the kinds of sky views northern and southern observers would see some time during the month.

▶ Key constellations

The maps in Chapter 3 provide a third level of information about particular constellations, which by their richness merit more detailed investigation than usual by eye, binoculars and telescope. They include the magnificent Sagittarius, which features dense star clouds, nebulae and clusters.

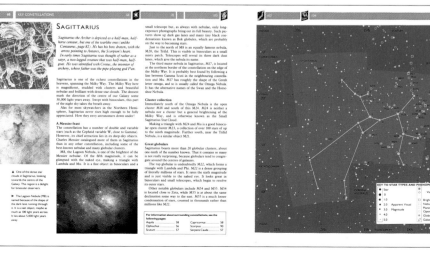

The maps

The first three chapters of the book focus on the stars and the constellations, and feature progressively more detailed star maps. The idea is that observers first become familiar with the shapes and locations of the constellations and then go on to investigate them in greater detail.

The main maps in Chapter 1 present the heavens season by season. They show the constellations that appear in the night sky in winter, spring, summer and autumn. Maps are included for both the Northern and the Southern Hemispheres. Half-circle sky views show the constellations visible looking west.

The main maps in Chapter 2 feature the stars and constellations prominent in the sky in particular months. They also include the brightest star clusters, nebulae and galaxies. Half-circle sky views help northern and southern observers orientate themselves. The maps in Chapter 3 present more information on outstanding constellations.

The maps in Chapter 4 feature the Moon. They cover the nearside – the one that always faces us – in four quadrants. The seas, the main craters, mountain ranges and other features of the lunar surface are marked.

Cross-referencing

The main text spreads in the book are concerned primarily with observation and practical astronomy in general. They can be read and appreciated quite independently of the reference spreads that appear at the end of each chapter. But if you want further information, you can turn to the reference spreads, using the icons appearing in the band at the top of each page.

If, for example, you are reading about the Orion Nebula and want to know more about nebulae, look for the "Nebula" icon in the band and note the number beside it (100). Turn to page 100 and you will find detailed information on nebulae. If, at any time, you want to refresh your memory on common astronomical terms, turn to the Glossary on pages 156 and 157.

The Lunar Surface

Outer Galaxies

Star Anatomy

Star Clusters

Moon Movements

The Milky Way

Nebulae

The Apollo Explorations

▶ Moon maps

The maps in Chapter 4 feature our nearest neighbour in space, the Moon. There are four maps, each covering one quadrant. The maps are printed with north at the top, and show the Moon as we see it with the naked eye and through binoculars. The maria (seas) and most prominent craters are marked.

◀ Reference spreads

This is an example of a reference spread. Reference spreads appear at the end of each chapter and provide background information on a range of topics.

▶ Cross-reference icons

Examples of the icons that appear, together with page numbers, in the band running along the top of ordinary text spreads. They refer to reference spreads focused on particular subjects.

◄ Fanciful figures that represent some constellations of the Northern Hemisphere. The zodiacal constellations Virgo, Libra, Scorpius and Sagittarius feature prominently in the picture, although Virgo and Libra are far from prominent in the heavens.

PATTERNS IN THE SKY

On a clear moonless night, the heavens present a dazzling spectacle. Myriads of twinkling stars sparkle like jewels against the velvety backcloth of space.

Even a quick glance at the night sky reveals that the stars are not all the same. Most obviously, they vary in brightness; they also show subtle variations in colour.

If we remain star-gazing for some time, we can easily learn to recognize the patterns the bright stars make – patterns we call the constellations. Familiarizing ourselves with the constellations is the first step in star-gazing, for they act as celestial signposts to help us find our way around the night sky.

Familiarizing ourselves with the constellations is the object of this chapter. We find out how and why they appear in, and disappear from, the night sky throughout the year, as one season gives way to the next.

The star maps represent the appearance of the late evening sky on significant seasonal dates – midwinter and midsummer and the equinoxes. Maps are included for both the Northern and the Southern Hemispheres.

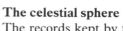

ANCIENT PATTERNS

The patterns of stars we see in the sky today will not change perceptibly in our lifetime. Indeed, they have changed scarcely at all since the time of the first great civilizations some 5,000 years ago.

In those days, priest-astronomers observed the rhythms of the heavens to establish calendars, which could bring a semblance of order into the day-to-day lives of an expanding population in an increasingly complex society. They also looked to the heavens for signs that would indicate the will of their gods, whom they believed ruled human lives. Their "reading the stars" led to the pseudo-science of astrology, which is still with us. Astrologers reckon that the relative positions of the heavenly bodies control human destiny.

▼ One of the most distinctive star patterns in the heavens is the constellation of Orion. It sits on the celestial equator and is therefore visible to star-gazers in both the Northern and the Southern Hemispheres. The sketch shows the way we join up the brightest stars to form the main constellation outline.

The celestial sphere

The records kept by those learned ancients show graphically that the constellations they were familiar with are virtually identical to those we see today. It seems, therefore, as if their concept of the heavens is valid. They considered the stars to be fixed in position on the inside of a great celestial sphere enveloping the Earth.

We now know that there is no great celestial sphere, but, nevertheless, the concept is useful in astronomy for it provides a convenient way of pinpointing the positions of the stars in the sky. (Turn to pages 34–5 to see how astronomers use it.)

The whirling heavens

If you remain star-gazing for any length of time, you notice that the stars move across the sky. They do not move relative to one another, but as a whole. In most parts of the world, if you follow a particular star throughout the night, you find that it first appears over the eastern horizon as darkness falls. Then it arcs up through the

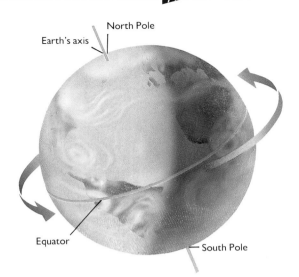

North Pole
Earth's axis
Equator
South Pole

▲ The reason why the stars
wheel overhead: the Earth
spins on its axis, making one
revolution a day. We show the
axis tilted to reflect the fact
that it is tilted in relation to
the direction it travels through
space.

sky, reaching its highest point in the south. It then arcs
down again, eventually disappearing over the western
horizon when daylight returns. Most of the stars arc
through the night sky in a similar way, travelling from
east to west, as the Sun does.

The celestial sphere, then, appears to be rotating from
east to west around the Earth. But actually, the reverse is
true. It is the Earth that is moving relative to the stars. It
spins round once a day on its axis, an imaginary line
passing through the North and South Poles.

It is because of the rotation of the Earth that we must
specify on a star map a particular time of night when the
stars will appear in the sky in the positions shown on the
map. At other times, the stars will appear in different
positions in the sky.

Changing with the seasons

If you look at the dome of the heavens over a period of
months, you will notice that some constellations are
always present. Others, however, come and go. This is a
consequence of the Earth's other motion in space – it
travels in orbit around the Sun once a year (see diagram,
right).

Again, from our Earth-bound viewpoint, it is the Sun
that appears to move. It appears to travel around the
celestial sphere against the background of stars once a
year. At any time, we will not be able to see the constellations that lie in the same direction as the Sun, because
the Sun's light will blot them out – it will be daylight. As
the Sun proceeds in its path around the celestial sphere
during the year (the ecliptic), different constellations will
be blotted out in turn while others return to dark skies.

The seasonal star maps

The maps that follow show views of the night sky as it
appears in late evening in mid-latitudes in the Northern
and Southern Hemispheres in midwinter and midsummer
and at the time of the March and September equinoxes.

The circular maps represent the dome of the heavens
above your head. Only the main constellations are shown.
Which of the constellations you will see at any instant
will depend on which direction you look in. As an example, we include on each spread a semicircular map that
shows the constellations you would see looking west.
West was chosen because it is an easy direction to find,
being the direction in which the Sun sets.

Using these maps will help you identify the constellations and get your celestial bearings as it were, season by
season. The maps most nearly represent the night sky
only at the specific time and on the specific dates chosen,
but for the purposes of constellation recognition and
general orientation, they are usable for much longer.

▼ Key points in the annual
orbit of the Earth around the
Sun. The tilt of the Earth's axis
always remains the same,
which means that each
hemisphere is angled more
towards the Sun at some times
of the year than at others. This
causes a difference in
temperature throughout the
year and brings about the
seasons. The dates are of
midsummer, midwinter and
the equinoxes. The seasons are
opposite in the Northern and
Southern Hemispheres.

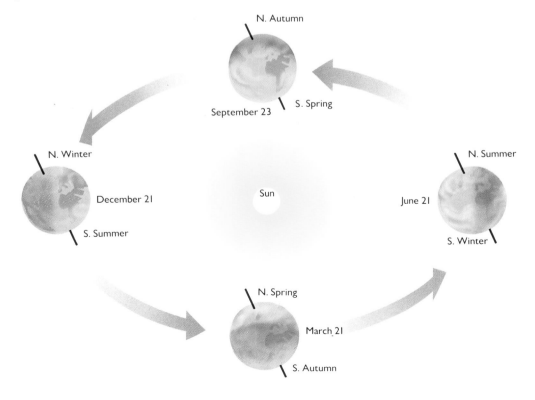

N. Autumn
September 23
S. Spring

N. Winter
December 21
S. Summer

Sun

N. Summer
June 21
S. Winter

N. Spring
March 21
S. Autumn

NORTHERN HEMISPHERE WINTER

Winter brings some of the most splendid constellations to northern skies, and they are seen at their best (weather permitting of course!) during the long, dark evenings.

Most magnificent of all is Orion, depicting the mighty hunter facing up to the charging bull Taurus. This constellation dominates the southern aspect of the sky, with its two brightest, first-magnitude stars Betelgeux and Rigel contrasting nicely in colour, the one noticeably red, the other pure white.

The three bright stars in Orion's "belt" act as pointers for locating two other celestial beacons, Aldebaran, which is higher in the sky; and Sirius, the Dog Star, which is lower. Aldebaran marks the angry red eye of Taurus, while Sirius (Canis Major), is the brightest star in the whole heavens.

And there are pleasures still to come. The pearly white arch of the Milky Way bisects the sky, separating Orion and Canis Major from Gemini and Canis Minor. Gemini boasts twin bright stars Castor and Pollux, while Canis Minor has just one, Procyon.

Overhead, at the zenith, on the edge of the Milky Way, is another beacon star Capella (Auriga). This completes a truly remarkable concentration, for the Northern Hemisphere at least, of eight first-magnitude stars.

The northern aspect of the sky shows Pegasus in the west, Leo in the east, and Cygnus in between, with the ever-brilliant Cassiopeia above it and also embedded in the Milky Way. The two stars at the share end of the Plough or Big Dipper, as always, point to the Pole Star, Polaris.

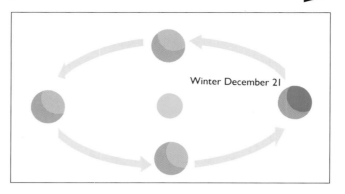

Winter December 21

THE CONSTELLATIONS DESCRIBED

To find details of the major constellations shown on the map, refer to the pages indicated below.

Andromeda	78	Columba	45	Lepus	45
Aries	64	Cygnus	84	Lyra	56
Auriga	44	Draco	40	Orion	86
Boötes	52	Eridanus	66	Pegasus	62
Cancer	46	Fornax	66	Perseus	67
Canes Venatici	50	Gemini	46	Pisces	63
Canis Major	44	Hercules	54	Taurus	92
Canis Minor	46	Hydra	48, 50	Triangulum	65
Cassiopeia	80	Lacerta	61	Ursa Major	94
Cepheus	40	Leo	48	Ursa Minor	40
Cetus	64				

USING THIS MAP

- This map represents the dome of the heavens at 11 pm local time on the date of the winter solstice, December 21.
- Because the stars rise about four minutes earlier each night, you will see a similar view of the heavens on December 14 at 11.30 pm and on December 28 at 10.30 pm.
- The centre of the map is your zenith. The edge of the map is your horizon. You may be able to see a little more or a little less north or south than the map shows, because your horizon depends on your latitude.

Looking south: To locate the constellations in the southern part of the sky, face south. The Sun will have set to your right. Hold the map in front of you with SOUTH at the bottom. The lower half of the map now represents the part of the sky in front of you.

Looking north: To locate the constellations in the northern part of the sky, face north. The Sun will have set to your left. Turn the map upside-down so that NORTH is at the bottom. The lower half of the map now represents the part of the sky in front of you.

Looking west

This hemisphere map shows the main constellations you would see looking west at about 11 pm local time on December 21. They may appear slightly higher or slightly lower in the sky, depending on your exact latitude.

The unmistakable W-shape of Cassiopeia and the Square of Pegasus are prominent.

Aldebaran
PERSEUS
TAURUS
Pleiades
ARIES
CASSIOPEIA
CEPHEUS
PEGASUS
Deneb
CETUS
CYGNUS

SOUTH   WEST   NORTH

KEY TO STAR TYPES AND PHENOMENA

●	Star
●	0
●	0.7
●	1.3 Apparent
●	2.0 Visual
●	2.7 Magnitude
·	3.3
·	4.0
⊙	Variable Stars
○	
⬭	Galaxy
✧	Globular Cluster

December 21

Northern Hemisphere Spring

With the coming of spring, Orion is setting by the late evening, although there is still plenty of time after sunset to view it.

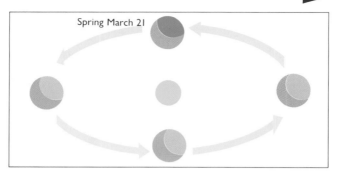

Spring March 21

The southern aspect of the sky in late evening belongs to Leo, whose distinctive back-to-front question mark star pattern (the Sickle) traces the Lion's head and mane.

Arcing south-west towards Orion, the twins Castor and Pollux (Gemini) are still prominent. Between Leo and Gemini, Cancer contains one of the top three star clusters in the northern heavens, Praesepe (Beehive).

Castor and Pollux are approximate pointers, aiming southwest, to the brighter Procyon (Canis Minor). Farther south, Canis Major and its prime star Sirius are close to setting.

In the east, the only two really bright stars are Spica (Virgo) and Arcturus (Boötes). Arcturus is a warm orange colour and the brightest star in the Northern Hemisphere.

The northern aspect of the sky reveals the Plough high up. Cassiopeia is fairly low in the north-west, pointing to the brilliant Capella (Auriga). Seemingly linked with Auriga is Taurus, whose chief star is Aldebaran. Its reddish hue contrasts noticeably with Capella's pure bluish white. Taurus's other main naked-eye attractions are its two prominent star clusters, the Hyades, surrounding Aldebaran, and the Pleiades, or Seven Sisters.

THE CONSTELLATIONS DESCRIBED

To find details of the major constellations shown on the map, refer to the pages indicated below.

Andromeda	78	Corona Borealis		Monoceros	47
Aries	64		54	Orion	86
Auriga	44	Cygnus	84	Perseus	67
Boötes	52	Draco	40	Pisces	63
Cancer	46	Eridanus	66	Puppis	47
Canes Venatici	50	Fornax	66	Serpens Caput	55
Canis Major	44	Gemini	46	Taurus	92
Canis Minor	46	Hercules	54	Triangulum	65
Cassiopeia	80	Hydra	48, 50	Ursa Major	94
Cepheus	40	Lacerta	61	Ursa Minor	40
Columba	45	Leo	48	Virgo	96
Coma Berenices	52	Lyra	56		

In the east Deneb (Cygnus) and Vega (Lyra) appear close to the horizon. The distinctive crescent of the Northern Crown (Corona Borealis) appears higher up.

USING THIS MAP

- This map represents the dome of the heavens at 11 pm local time on the date of the spring, or vernal equinox, March 21.
- Because the stars rise about four minutes earlier each night, you will see a similar view of the heavens on March 14 at 11.30 pm and on March 28 at 10.30 pm.
- The centre of the map is your zenith. The edge of the map is your horizon. You may be able to see a little more or a little less north or south than the map shows, because your horizon depends on your latitude.

Looking south: To locate the constellations in the southern part of the sky, face south. The Sun will have set to your right. Hold the map in front of you with SOUTH at the bottom. The lower half of the map now represents the part of the sky in front of you.

Looking north: To locate the constellations in the northern part of the sky, face north. The Sun will have set to your left. Turn the map upside-down so that NORTH is at the bottom. The lower half of the map now represents the part of the sky in front of you.

Looking west

This hemisphere map shows the main constellations you would see looking west at about 11 pm local time on March 21. They may appear slightly higher or slightly lower in the sky, depending on your exact latitude.

This view boasts a collection of bright stars, including Sirius, Betelgeux and Capella.

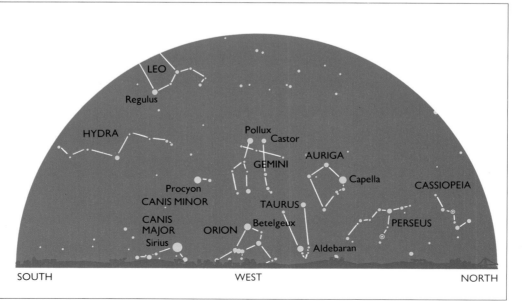

KEY TO STAR TYPES AND PHENOMENA

Star	
0	
0.7	
1.3	Apparent
2.0	Visual
2.7	Magnitude
3.3	
4.0	
Variable Stars	
Galaxy	
Globular Cluster	

March 21

N

CYGNUS Deneb
CEPHEUS
CASSIOPEIA
M31
ANDROMEDA

LYRA
Vega
DRACO
Polaris
URSA MINOR
PERSEUS
HERCULES
Capella AURIGA
TAURUS
Pleiades

CORONA
BOR.
URSA MAJOR
Aldebaran

E
OPHIUCHUS
BOÖTES
GEMINI
ORION
W
SERPENS
(Caput)
Castor
Pollux
Arcturus
Betelgeux
Rigel
CANCER
LEO
CANIS
MINOR
Regulus
Procyon

VIRGO
HYDRA

LIBRA
Spica
Sirius
CANIS
MAJOR
CORVUS
PUPPIS

CENTAURUS
VELA

S

NORTHERN HEMISPHERE SUMMER

The warmer nights make summer star-gazing a pleasure, although their drawback is that the skies are never really dark.

High in the sky at this time of the summer solstice are three first-magnitude stars, Deneb (Cygnus), Vega (Lyra) and Altair (Aquila). They form the celebrated Summer Triangle. It overlays a rich region of the Milky Way, although this is difficult to appreciate fully because of the light skies.

Deneb, in the tail of the flying Swan, is the dimmest of the summer trio, at least to the eye. In reality it is thousands of times more luminous, appearing dimmer only because it is more than 60 and 100 times farther away respectively than Vega and Altair.

Deneb shines high in the north-east, while above the eastern horizon is Andromeda and part of the Square of Pegasus, which will become prominent in autumn skies. Leo, meanwhile, is about to set in the far west.

The other two stars of the Summer Triangle, Vega and Altair, appear in south-eastern skies, the one high up, the other midway to the horizon. Rising just above the horizon here are portions of two of the splendid Southern Hemisphere constellations that northern astronomers drool over. They are Sagittarius and, nearly due south, Scorpius, whose pulsating red supergiant star Antares

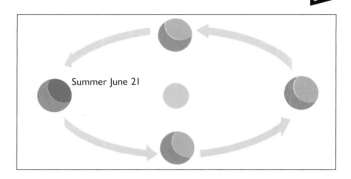

Summer June 21

THE CONSTELLATIONS DESCRIBED

To find details of the major constellations shown on the map, refer to the pages indicated below.

Andromeda	78	Delphinus	58	Pegasus	62
Aquarius	60	Draco	40	Perseus	67
Aquila	58	Eridanus	66	Puppis	47
Auriga	44	Fornax	66	Sagittarius	88
Boötes	52	Gemini	46	Scorpius	90
Cancer	46	Hercules	54	Scutum	57
Canes Venatici	50	Lacerta	61	Serpens Caput	55
Cassiopeia	80	Leo	48	Serpens Cauda	57
Cepheus	40	Libra	53	Ursa Major	94
Columba	45	Lynx	49	Ursa Minor	40
Coma Berenices	52	Lyra	56	Virgo	96
Corona Borealis	54	Monoceros	47	Vulpecula	59
Cygnus	84	Ophiuchus	56		

("Rival of Mars") marks the Scorpion's heart.

Antares forms one corner of a more widely separated "summer triangle" with Spica (Virgo), at about the same elevation, and Arcturus (Boötes) farther north.

USING THIS MAP

- This map represents the dome of the heavens at 11 pm local time on the date of the summer solstice, June 21.
- Because the stars rise about four minutes earlier each night, you will see a similar view of the heavens on June 14 at 11.30 pm and on June 28 at 10.30 pm.
- The centre of the map is your zenith. The edge of the map is your horizon. You may be able to see a little more or a little less north or south than the map shows, because your horizon depends on your latitude.

Looking south: To locate the constellations in the southern part of the sky, face south. The Sun will have set to your right. Hold the map in front of you with SOUTH at the bottom. The lower half of the map now represents the part of the sky in front of you.

Looking north: To locate the constellations in the northern part of the sky, face north. The Sun will have set to your left. Turn the map upside-down so that NORTH is at the bottom. The lower half of the map now represents the part of the sky in front of you.

Looking west

This hemisphere map shows the main constellations you would see looking west at about 11 pm local time on June 21. They may appear slightly higher or slightly lower in the sky, depending on your exact latitude.

Arcturus straight ahead forms a prominent triangle with Antares and Spica to the south.

KEY TO STAR TYPES AND PHENOMENA

●	Star	
●	0	
●	0.7	
●	1.3	Apparent
●	2.0	Visual
●	2.7	Magnitude
·	3.3	
·	4.0	
⊙	Variable Stars	
○		
⬭	Galaxy	
✳	Globular Cluster	

June 21

NORTHERN HEMISPHERE AUTUMN

With evening skies darkening perceptibly, the Milky Way can now be better appreciated as it cuts across the sky from north-east to south-west.

Looking south, this silvery arch carries with it Cygnus high overhead, and Aquila lower down. The Summer Triangle, formed by their two main stars, Deneb and Altair, together with Vega (Lyra), is still conspicuous, though not for long.

The late evening sky is now graced by Pegasus with its unmistakable Square. The two stars in the westernmost side of the Square act as pointers to Fomalhaut (Piscis Austrinus), just visible above the southern horizon.

The line of stars running east from the northern side of the Square belong to Andromeda. This constellation's main claim to fame is the fuzzy patch of light we can see just to the north of the line of stars. This patch, once thought to be a nebula in our own Galaxy, turns out to be a quite separate galaxy, much bigger than our own but incredibly distant (some 22 million million million kilometres/13.5 million million million miles!).

Looking north, the Plough is near its lowest point, while on the other side of Polaris, Cassiopeia is near its highest. While much of Boötes is visible in the north-west, its bright star Arcturus is below the horizon. Close by is the distinctive curve of the Northern Crown (Corona Borealis).

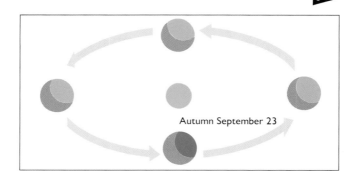

Autumn September 23

THE CONSTELLATIONS DESCRIBED

To find details of the major constellations shown on the map, refer to the pages indicated below.

Andromeda	78	Corona Borealis	54	Piscis Austrinus	61
Aquarius	60	Cygnus	84	Puppis	47
Aquila	58	Delphinus	58	Sagittarius	88
Aries	64	Draco	40	Sculptor	63
Auriga	44	Hercules	54	Scutum	57
Boötes	52	Hydra	48, 50	Serpens Caput	55
Cancer	46	Lacerta	61	Serpens Cauda	57
Canes Venatici	50	Lynx	49	Taurus	92
Canis Minor	46	Lyra	56	Triangulum	65
Capricornus	58	Ophiuchus	56	Ursa Major	94
Cassiopeia	80	Pegasus	62	Ursa Minor	40
Cepheus	40	Perseus	67	Vulpecula	59
Cetus	64	Pisces	63		
Columba	45				

There is more interest, however, in the east where Auriga and Taurus have now risen, with their two brilliant main stars, Capella and Aldebaran, set for prominence in winter skies.

USING THIS MAP
● This map represents the dome of the heavens at 11 pm local time on the date of the autumnal equinox, September 23.
● Because the stars rise about four minutes earlier each night, you will see a similar view of the heavens on September 16 at 11.30 pm and on September 30 at 10.30 pm.
● The centre of the map is your zenith. The edge of the map is your horizon. You may be able to see a little more or a little less north or south than the map shows, because your horizon depends on your latitude.
Looking south: To locate the constellations in the southern part of the sky, face south. The Sun will have set to your right. Hold the map in front of you with SOUTH at the bottom. The lower half of the map now represents the part of the sky in front of you.
Looking north: To locate the constellations in the northern part of the sky, face north. The Sun will have set to your left. Turn the map upside-down so that NORTH is at the bottom. The lower half of the map now represents the part of the sky in front of you.

Looking west

This hemisphere map shows the main constellations you would see looking west at about 11 pm local time on September 23. They may appear slightly higher or slightly lower in the sky, depending on your exact latitude.

The three stars of the Summer Triangle – Altair, Deneb and Vega – are straight ahead.

SOUTH   WEST   NORTH

KEY TO STAR TYPES AND PHENOMENA

	Star
	0
	0.7
	1.3 Apparent
	2.0 Visual
	2.7 Magnitude
	3.3
	4.0
⊚	Variable Stars
○	
⬭	Galaxy
✳	Globular Cluster

September 23

SOUTHERN HEMISPHERE SUMMER

While astronomers in the Northern Hemisphere shiver in midwinter, their colleagues "down under" in the Southern Hemisphere enjoy the balmy nights of mid-summer.

As in the Northern Hemisphere, Orion is a dominant constellation, seen by southern astronomers in the northern aspect of the sky. They see it with white Rigel in the upper left of the main pattern, and the reddish Betelgeux in the bottom right.

Following a line through the three stars of Orion's "belt" leads higher up to the brightest star in the heavens, Sirius (Canis Major) and lower down to the reddish Aldebaran (Taurus). Continuing the same line through Aldebaran leads to the Pleiades, or Seven Sisters, star cluster. And near the horizon beneath Aldebaran is the brighter Capella (Auriga).

East of Capella are the twins, Castor and Pollux (Gemini), with the brilliant Procyon (Canis Minor) higher up. The brilliant stars in this corner of the sky together form a prominent hexagonal pattern.

The southern aspect of the sky, as always in the Southern Hemisphere, is spectacular. The second brightest star in the heavens, Canopus (Carina), sits high in the sky, as does Achernar (Eridanus) farther west. Farther west still and lower is Fomalhaut (Piscis Austrinus).

The Southern Cross (Crux) and its two pointers, Alpha

and Beta Centauri (Centaurus), are stunning as always, and seen relatively close to the horizon. The fuzzy patches we see south-west of Canopus are neighbouring galaxies, the Large (Doradus) and Small Magellanic Cloud (Tucana).

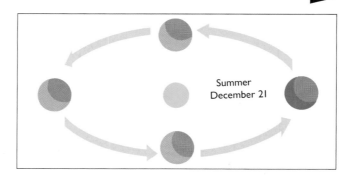

Summer
December 21

THE CONSTELLATIONS DESCRIBED

To find details of the major constellations shown on the map, refer to the pages indicated below.

Aries	64	Dorado	42	Perseus	67
Auriga	44	Eridanus	66	Phoenix	62
Cancer	46	Fornax	66	Pisces	63
Canis Major	44	Gemini	46	Piscis Austrinus	61
Canis Minor	46	Grus	60	Puppis	47
Carina	42	Hydra	48, 50	Sculptor	63
Centaurus	82	Lepus	45	Taurus	92
Cetus	64	Monoceros	47	Triangulum	65
Columba	45	Orion	86	Tucana	42
Crux	82				

USING THIS MAP

- This map represents the dome of the heavens at 11 pm local time on the date of the summer solstice, December 21.
- Because the stars rise about four minutes earlier each night, you will see a similar view of the heavens on December 14 at 11.30 pm and on December 28 at 10.30 pm.
- The centre of the map is your zenith. The edge of the map is your horizon. You may be able to see a little more or a little less north or south than the map shows, because your horizon depends on your latitude.

Looking north: To locate the constellations in the northern part of the sky, face north. The Sun will have set to your left. Hold the map in front of you with NORTH at the bottom. The lower half of the map now represents the part of the sky in front of you.

Looking south: To locate the constellations in the southern part of the sky, face south. The Sun will have set to your right. Turn the map upside-down so that SOUTH is at the bottom. The lower half of the map now represents the part of the sky in front of you.

Looking west

This hemisphere map shows the main constellations you would see looking west at about 11 pm local time on December 21. They may appear slightly higher or slightly lower in the sky, depending on your exact latitude.

Rather a bare sky. Aldebaran and the Pleiades cluster lie in the north.

SOUTH   WEST   NORTH

KEY TO STAR TYPES AND PHENOMENA

●	Star
●	0
●	0.7
●	1.3 Apparent
●	2.0 Visual
●	2.7 Magnitude
·	3.3
·	4.0
⊙	Variable Stars
○	
⬭	Galaxy
✦	Globular Cluster

DECEMBER 21

S

ARA

CRUX

α
β

�※ ω
CENTAURUS

GRUS

47
�※ SMC

PISCIS
AUS.

LMC

Fomalhaut

CORVUS

PHOENIX

Achernar

CARINA

VELA

Canopus

W   AQUARIUS

COLUMBA

PUPPIS

HYDRA

E

ERIDANUS

LEPUS

CANIS
MAJOR

CETUS

Sirius

Rigel

Regulus

PEGASUS

PISCES

ORION

Procyon

CANIS
MINOR

CANCER

Betelgeux

ARIES   TAURUS   Aldebaran

Pleiades

Pollux

ANDRO—
MEDA

GEMINI   Castor

AURIGA

Capella

PERSEUS

N

SOUTHERN HEMISPHERE AUTUMN

The bright starscapes of winter no longer dominate the northern aspect of the sky in the late evening. Orion, Gemini, Canis Major and Minor are fast slipping away in the west.

It is Leo that now occupies centre stage, with its hook-like pattern of stars "hanging" from the first-magnitude Regulus. Two other bright stars lie to the east. Spica (Virgo) at about the same elevation as Regulus (Leo) and Arcturus (Boötes) lower down. The remainder of the sky is relatively barren, because of the sprawling constellation Hydra near the zenith, which has no bright stars at all.

Turning to the southern aspect, this is occupied by a great swathe of the Milky Way, with more than its fair share of stellar delights. These range from the Southern Cross (Crux) and Alpha and Beta Centauri (Centaurus) high up, to the wickedly curved tail of Scorpius, the Scorpion, which is just appearing over the eastern horizon and will become one of winter's great pleasures.

The longer arm of the Southern Cross points almost to the celestial south pole. But there is no convenient bright star to mark the pole's position as there is in the Northern Hemisphere (Polaris, the Pole Star).

But the Cross does point more or less in the direction of the Small Magellanic Cloud (Tucana), located on the other side of the pole. The Large Magellanic Cloud (Dorado) is located higher up, in the direction of the

brilliant Canopus (Carina). The two Clouds form a triangle with Achernar, the only bright star in Eridanus, recently risen above the horizon.

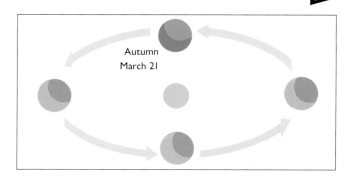

Autumn
March 21

THE CONSTELLATIONS DESCRIBED

To find details of the major constellations shown on the map, refer to the pages indicated below.

USING THIS MAP

• This map represents the dome of the heavens at 11 pm local time on the date of the March equinox, March 21.

• Because the stars rise about four minutes earlier each night, you will see a similar view of the heavens on March 14 at 11.30 pm and on March 28 at 10.30 pm.

• The centre of the map is your zenith. The edge of the map is your horizon. You may be able to see a little more or a little less north or south than the map shows, because your horizon depends on your latitude.

Looking north: To locate the constellations in the northern part of the sky, face north. The Sun will have set to your left. Hold the map in front of you with NORTH at the bottom. The lower half of the map now represents the part of the sky in front of you.

Looking south: To locate the constellations in the southern part of the sky, face south. The Sun will have set to your right. Turn the map upside-down so that SOUTH is at the bottom. The lower half of the map now represents the part of the sky in front of you.

Looking west

This hemisphere map shows the main constellations you would see looking west at about 11 pm local time on March 21. They may appear slightly higher or slightly lower in the sky, depending on your exact latitude.

An abundance of bright stars graces western skies this month, led by Sirius and Canopus.

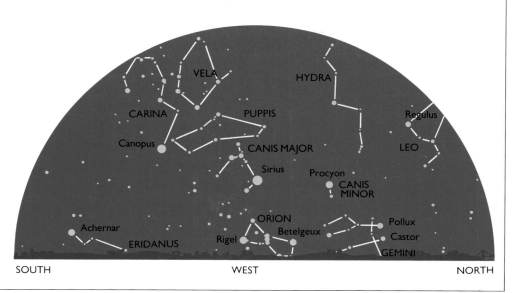

SOUTH   WEST   NORTH

KEY TO STAR TYPES AND PHENOMENA

Star	
0	
0.7	
1.3	Apparent
2.0	Visual
2.7	Magnitude
3.3	
4.0	
	Variable Stars
	Galaxy
	Globular Cluster

March 21

SOUTHERN HEMISPHERE WINTER

The winter skies in the Southern Hemisphere are the stamping ground of the Scorpion (Scorpius), whose curved tail is poised ready to deal a deadly sting. The constellation is high overhead, instantly recognizable and breathtaking in its beauty. The brightest star, the red Antares, lies near the zenith.

Cheek-by-jowl with the Scorpion in what is the richest part of the Milky Way is Sagittarius. This constellation overflows with astronomical delights, which binoculars show to perfection. There are dense and brilliant star clouds, swirling nebulae and scattered star clusters. The reason why the Milky Way appears so dense here is because the centre of our Galaxy lies in this direction.

The northern aspect of the sky shows, south of Sagittarius and also in the Milky Way, the bright Altair (Aquila). Vega (Lyra) farther south and east rises later, while Deneb (Cygnus) rises later still. These three stars form a prominent winter triangle, which northern astronomers call the Summer Triangle to match their own season.

The higher of the only two prominent stars in the north-west is Spica (Virgo); the lower is Arcturus (Boötes). Close by is the half-circle of stars known as the Northern Crown (Corona Borealis), which is so much easier to place than its southern equivalent.

The southern aspect of the winter sky reveals the

Southern Cross (Crux) and its bright pointers Alpha and Beta Centauri (Centaurus) descending. Alpha Centauri is the nearest bright star to us, a "mere" 4.3 light years, or some 40 million million kilometres (25 million million miles) away.

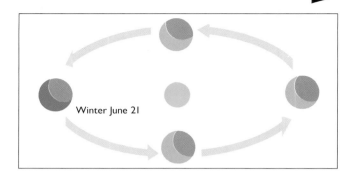

Winter June 21

THE CONSTELLATIONS DESCRIBED

To find details of the major constellations shown on the map, refer to the pages indicated below.

Aquarius	60	Delphinus	58	Phoenix	62
Aquila	58	Dorado	42	Piscis Austrinus	61
Ara	42	Eridanus	66	Puppis	47
Boötes	52	Grus	60	Sagittarius	88
Canes Venatici	50	Hercules	54	Scorpius	90
Capricornus	58	Hydra	48, 50	Scutum	57
Carina	42	Leo	48	Serpens Caput	55
Centaurus	82	Libra	53	Serpens Cauda	57
Coma Berenices	52	Lupus	53	Tucana	42
Corona Borealis	54	Lyra	56	Vela	49
Crux	82	Ophiuchus	56	Virgo	96

USING THIS MAP

● This map represents the dome of the heavens at 11 pm local time on the date of the winter solstice, June 21.

● Because the stars rise about four minutes earlier each night, you will see a similar view of the heavens on June 14 at 11.30 pm and on June 28 at 10.30 pm.

● The centre of the map is your zenith. The edge of the map is your horizon. You may be able to see a little more or a little less north or south than the map shows, because your horizon depends on your latitude.

Looking north: To locate the constellations in the northern part of the sky, face north. The Sun will have set to your left. Hold the map in front of you with NORTH at the bottom. The lower half of the map now represents the part of the sky in front of you.

Looking south: To locate the constellations in the southern part of the sky, face south. The Sun will have set to your right. Turn the map upside-down so that SOUTH is at the bottom. The lower half of the map now represents the part of the sky in front of you.

Looking west

This hemisphere map shows the main constellations you would see looking west at about 11 pm local time on June 21. They may appear slightly higher or slightly lower in the sky, depending on your exact latitude.

Alpha, Beta and Omega Centauri and Crux are bright in the south; Arcturus in the north.

SOUTH   WEST   NORTH

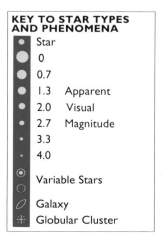

KEY TO STAR TYPES AND PHENOMENA

●	Star
●	0
●	0.7
●	1.3 Apparent
●	2.0 Visual
●	2.7 Magnitude
·	3.3
·	4.0
⊙	Variable Stars
○	
⬭	Galaxy
✳	Globular Cluster

June 21

S

DORADO

Canopus

ERIDANUS

LMC

CARINA

Achernar

PHOENIX

SMC
✵ 47

VELA

CRUX

GRUS

β α

Fomalhaut

HYDRA

✵ ω

PISCIS AUS.

CENTAURUS

ARA

W

CORVUS

LUPUS

CAPRICORNUS

SCORPIUS

AQUARIUS

VIRGO   Spica

LIBRA

Antares

SAGITTARIUS

PEGASUS

SERPENS
(Cauda)

OPHIUCHUS

Altair

AQUILA

Arcturus

SERPENS
(Caput)

BOÖTES

CORONA
BOR.

LYRA

CYGNUS

HERCULES

Vega

Deneb

N

E

SOUTHERN HEMISPHERE SPRING

The great delights of winter skies, Sagittarius and Scorpius, are now seen in the south-west. They are still well placed for viewing, but in the next few weeks they will disappear from the late evening skies.

Still looking south, the Southern Cross (Crux) and its pointers, Alpha and Beta Centauri (Centaurus), are now low down on the horizon. So is the "False Cross", formed by a pair of stars in Vela and a pair in Carina.

The Magellanic Clouds are particularly well placed for observation, the Small Cloud appearing nearly due south and the Large Cloud (Dorado) more to the east and lower down.

The two Clouds are more or less in line with the brilliant Canopus (Carina), a star only exceeded in brightness by Sirius (Canis Major), which is just rising (or about to rise, depending on the observer's latitude) above the eastern horizon.

The northern aspect of the spring sky shows the Square of Pegasus prominent. The showpiece constellations of summer, Taurus and Orion, are about to rise in the east. The Pleiades, or Seven Sisters, star cluster may well be already above the horizon.

High overhead, near the zenith, Fomalhaut (Piscis Austrinus) is conspicuous, not because it is outstandingly bright but because it appears in a relatively barren part of the heavens.

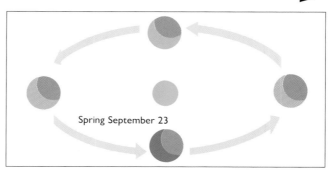

Spring September 23

THE CONSTELLATIONS DESCRIBED

To find details of the major constellations shown on the map, refer to the pages indicated below.

Andromeda 78	Columba 45	Ophiuchus 56
Aquarius 60	Crux 82	Pegasus 62
Aquila 58	Cygnus 84	Phoenix 62
Ara 42	Delphinus 58	Pisces 63
Aries 64	Dorado 42	Sagittarius 88
Capricornus 58	Eridanus 66	Serpens Cauda 57
Carina 42	Grus 60	Scorpius 90
Centaurus 82	Lupus 53	Scutum 57
Cetus 64	Lyra 56	

In the north-west two or even three stars of the "winter triangle" may still be visible. Altair (Aquila) is relatively high in the sky, while Deneb (Cygnus) is close to setting, and Vega (Lyra) may have set already.

USING THIS MAP

• This map represents the dome of the heavens at 11 pm local time on the date of the September equinox, September 23.

• Because the stars rise about four minutes earlier each night, you will see a similar view of the heavens on September 16 at 11.30 pm and on September 30 at 10.30 pm.

• The centre of the map is your zenith. The edge of the map is your horizon. You may be able to see a little more or a little less north or south than the map shows, because your horizon depends on your latitude.

Looking north: To locate the constellations in the northern part of the sky, face north. The Sun will have set to your left. Hold the map in front of you with NORTH at the bottom. The lower half of the map now represents the part of the sky in front of you.

Looking south: To locate the constellations in the southern part of the sky, face south. The Sun will have set to your right. Turn the map upside-down so that SOUTH is at the bottom. The lower half of the map now represents the part of the sky in front of you.

Looking west

This hemisphere map shows the main constellations you would see looking west at about 11 pm local time on September 23. They may appear slightly higher or slightly lower in the sky, depending on your exact latitude.

The Milky Way is almost horizontal and low down, and boasts delights galore.

SOUTH   WEST   NORTH

KEY TO STAR TYPES AND PHENOMENA

Star	
0	
0.7	
1.3	Apparent
2.0	Visual
2.7	Magnitude
3.3	
4.0	
Variable Stars	
Galaxy	
Globular Cluster	

September 23

THE CONSTELLATIONS

Observational astronomy hinges on the star patterns we call the constellations, which enable us quickly to find a particular star in the heavens. The constellations do not appear to change century after century. Their stars seem to be fixed in position and travel as a group through space. This, however, is an illusion.

▼ Constellations of the Northern Hemisphere, featured in an ancient astronomy book. The artist has used his imagination to create some interesting characters. Behind each one, there is a fascinating mythological story of love, lust, jealousy, hate, heroism and sacrifice.

The stars in the constellations are not in fact grouped together in space. They are quite independent of one another and are usually separated by vast distances. We see them together in the sky merely because they happen to lie in the same direction in space. For example, of the seven brightest stars in the familiar constellation Orion, the closest (Gamma) lies about 300 light years away, while the most distant (Kappa) lies over 1,800 light years away.

Again, the stars in the constellations appear to be fixed in position, but they are not. They are all moving through space, at different speeds and in different directions. But they lie so very far away from us that, except in a few cases, their movement is imperceptible. Only after tens of thousands of years will the star patterns we see today show noticeable changes.

Naming the constellations
Altogether, there are 88 recognized constellations (see opposite). Many of them date back at least 5,000 years. We know this from the records kept by ancient star-gazers in the Middle East – in Babylon and Egypt.

But it is to the ancient Greeks that we are indebted for the names of most of the constellations that we use today, although we use the Latin form of the Greek names. We also often call the constellations by their translated names. For example, the constellation Ursa Major translates into English as the Great Bear, Leo as the Lion and Cygnus as the Swan.

Myths and monsters
The Greeks named the constellations after gods, heroes, creatures and objects that featured in their mythology, matching the star patterns to the mythological figures. For many constellations you need an active imagination to see the resemblance between the figure and the star pattern it is meant to represent.

However, in some instances, the constellation patterns really do look like the figures they are intended to represent. Scorpius, for example, really does look like a scorpion, with a wicked curved tail. Cygnus really does look like a flying swan, with its long neck outstretched. Ursa Major can with a little imagination turn into a bear, and Leo into a lion.

Ptolemy and Bayer
The Greeks recognized some 48 constellations. The last great ancient Greek astronomer Ptolemy listed them in his celebrated encyclopaedia of astronomy and mathematics (*circa* AD 140), which has come down to us in its Arab translation, known as the *Almagest*.

Forty constellations were later added, notably by the German astronomers Johann Bayer (in 1603) and Johann Hevelius (in 1690) and the French astronomer Nicolas Lacaille (in 1752).

Bayer also introduced the system of using letters of the Greek alphabet to identify the stars in a constellation. He designated the brightest star Alpha (α), the second brightest Beta (β), the third brightest Gamma (γ) and so on. Bayer was not always accurate in grading the stars in this way; nevertheless astronomers still follow the designations he adopted.

1 Andromeda
2 Antlia, Air Pump
3 Apus, Bird of Paradise
4 Aquarius, Water-Bearer
5 Aquila, Eagle
6 Ara, Altar
7 Aries, Ram
8 Auriga, Charioteer
9 Boötes, Herdsman
10 Caelum, Graving Tool
11 Camelopardalis, Giraffe
12 Cancer, Crab
13 Canes Venatici, Hunting Dogs
14 Canis Major, Great Dog
15 Canis Minor, Little Dog
16 Capricornus, Sea Goat
17 Carina, Keel
18 Cassiopeia
19 Centaurus, Centaur
20 Cepheus
21 Cetus, Whale
22 Chamaeleon, Chameleon
23 Circinus, Compasses
24 Columba, Dove
25 Coma Berenices, Berenice's Hair

26 Corona Australis, Southern Crown
27 Corona Borealis, Northern Crown
28 Corvus, Crow
29 Crater, Cup
30 Crux, Southern Cross
31 Cygnus, Swan
32 Delphinus, Dolphin
33 Dorado, Swordfish
34 Draco, Dragon
35 Equuleus, Foal
36 Eridanus
37 Fornax, Furnace
38 Gemini, Twins
39 Grus, Crane
40 Hercules
41 Horologium, Clock
42 Hydra, Water Snake
43 Hydrus, Little Snake
44 Indus, Indian
45 Lacerta, Lizard
46 Leo, Lion
47 Leo Minor, Little Lion
48 Lepus, Hare
49 Libra, Scales

Northern Hemisphere

Southern Hemisphere

50 Lupus, Wolf
51 Lynx, Lynx
52 Lyra, Lyre
53 Mensa, Table
54 Microscopium, Microscope
55 Monoceros, Unicorn
56 Musca, Fly
57 Norma, Rule
58 Octans, Octant
59 Ophiuchus, Serpent-Bearer
60 Orion
61 Pavo, Peacock
62 Pegasus, Flying Horse
63 Perseus
64 Phoenix, Phoenix
65 Pictor, Painter
66 Pisces, Fishes
67 Piscis Austrinus, Southern Fish
68 Puppis, Poop
69 Pyxis, Compass

70 Reticulum, Net
71 Sagitta, Arrow
72 Sagittarius, Archer
73 Scorpius, Scorpion
74 Sculptor, Sculptor
75 Scutum, Shield
76 Serpens, Serpent
77 Sextans, Sextant
78 Taurus, Bull
79 Telescopium, Telescope
80 Triangulum, Triangle
81 Triangulum Australe, Southern Triangle
82 Tucana, Toucan
83 Ursa Major, Great Bear
84 Ursa Minor, Little Bear
85 Vela, Sails
86 Virgo, Virgin
87 Volans, Flying Fish
88 Vulpecula, Fox

The concept of the celestial sphere, with labels: North celestial pole, Direction of rotation, Sun, Earth's equator, Ecliptic, Celestial sphere, Celestial equator, South celestial pole.

The *celestial equator* is a circle around the celestial sphere midway between the celestial poles; it is a projection of the Earth's Equator. The stars follow paths parallel with the celestial equator.

An observer's view of the celestial sphere is bounded all around by the *horizon*, where the horizontal plane through the observer's position meets the sphere. The point on the celestial sphere directly above the observer's head is the *zenith*. The equivalent point on the sphere directly beneath the observer is the *nadir*.

The great circle passing through the north celestial pole, the zenith, and the south celestial pole is the *meridian*. Stars *culminate*, or reach their highest altitude, on the meridian.

The *ecliptic* is the apparent path of the Sun around the celestial sphere during the year. The Sun crosses the celestial equator on March 21, moving north; and on September 23, moving south. On these dates, day and night are exactly 12 hours long all over the world. That is why they are called the equinoxes ("equal nights").

▲ The concept of the celestial sphere: the stars are stuck on the inside of the sphere in fixed positions. The Earth is at the centre and is stationary; the celestial sphere rotates around it from east to west.

▼ Observers in mid-latitudes will see the north celestial pole midway between the zenith and the horizon. They will see the stars rise in the east, arc through the sky, and then set in the west. The stars near the north celestial pole will describe complete circles and will always be visible.

► Star trails over the Roque de los Muchachos Observatory on La Palma in the Canary Islands. The two domes house the 1-metre (39-inch) Jacobus Kapteyn Telescope (*left*) and the 2.5-metre (98-inch) Isaac Newton Telescope. The view shows stars circling the north celestial pole.

THE CELESTIAL SPHERE

We noted earlier that here on Earth we seem to be at the centre of a great enveloping heavenly or celestial sphere, which rotates around us from east to west carrying the stars and the other heavenly bodies with it.

Although we know that there is no such thing as a celestial sphere and that the motion of the heavenly bodies is an apparent one, created by the Earth spinning on its axist from west to east, the idea is still useful to observational astronomy. The two diagrams on this page show features of the sphere that astronomers frequently refer to.

The *north and south celestial poles* are points on the celestial sphere that lie directly above the Earth's North and South Poles respectively. The sphere appears to rotate on an axis through the celestial poles. The star Polaris lies very close to the north celestial pole and is called the Pole Star. There is no convenient bright star near the south celestial pole.

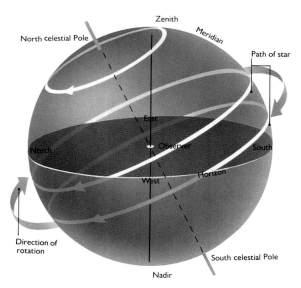

Diagram with labels: Zenith, Meridian, North celestial Pole, Path of star, East, Observer, South, North, West, Horizon, Direction of rotation, South celestial Pole, Nadir.

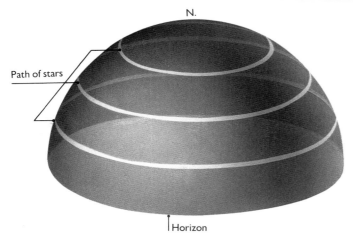

Path of stars

N.

Horizon

Observers at the North and South Poles and on the Equator view the heavens in quite a different way from everyone else. At the North Pole, for example (*left*), they will see the stars moving parallel with the horizon. On the Equator (*right*) the stars rise and set vertically. So if they look east or west, they will see the stars move straight up or straight down.

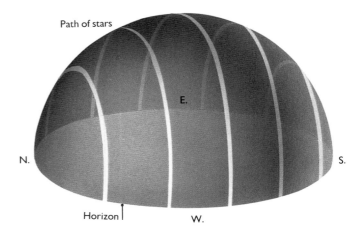

Path of stars

N.   E.   S.

Horizon   W.

Celestial time

The spinning of the Earth on its axis provides the basis for measuring time. Our day of 24 hours is the time it takes the Earth to spin round once and return to the same position in the sky *relative to the Sun*. We call this, our ordinary time, "solar time".

At first sight, we might also expect the celestial sphere to rotate around us in 24 hours. But it does not. If you note the time when a certain star rises above the horizon on successive days, you will find that on the second day the star rises four minutes earlier than on the first, and that on the third day it rises four minutes earlier still, and so on.

In other words, the celestial sphere rotates once around the Earth in 23 hours 56 minutes. Or, put the other way round, the Earth rotates once *relative to the stars* in 23 hours 56 minutes. This is the Earth's true period of rota-

tion and forms the basis of what we call "sidereal time", or time *relative to the stars*.

When they are observing, astronomers use sidereal time. Then the stars rise, culminate and set at the same time. In other words, they are in the same position in the sky at the same time.

Pinpointing the stars

Many of the brightest stars are easily located because they form part of the recognizable pattern of a constellation. But other stars are more difficult to pinpoint accurately. Astronomers therefore follow geographers on Earth and locate stars by a stellar "map reference". The method they use is exactly analogous to the system of terrestrial latitude and longitude.

The latitude of a point on Earth is the angular distance the point is north or south of the Equator. It is

▼ The Sun crosses the celestial equator at two points on its annual path (ecliptic) around the celestial sphere. It crosses at the vernal equinox (March 21) at a point called the First Point in Aries, and at the autumnal equinox (September 23) at the First Point in Libra.

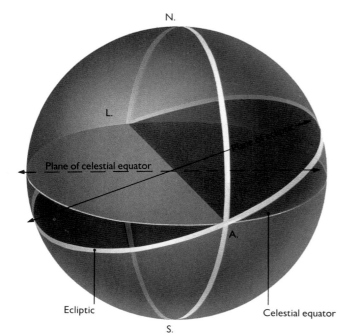

N.

L.

Plane of celestial equator

A.

Ecliptic

Celestial equator

S.

Celestial co-ordinates
We pinpoint the position of a star on the celestial sphere by a system of celestial latitude (declination) and longitude (right ascension). The declination (δ) is the angular distance of the star from the celestial equator. It is measured in degrees.

The right ascension (RA) is the angular distance of the star along the celestial equator from the First Point in Aries. This is the point where the Sun's path (the ecliptic) crosses the celestial equator in spring. Right ascension is measured in hours and minutes.

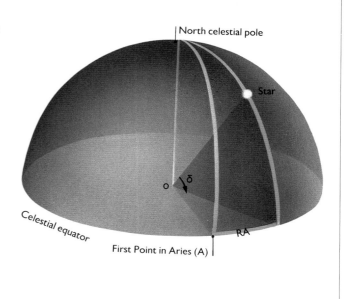

North celestial pole

Star

δ

o δ

Celestial equator

First Point in Aries (A)

RA

measured in degrees and minutes. The celestial latitude, or declination, of a star is the angular distance the star is north or south of the celestial equator. It, too, is measured in degrees and minutes. Declinations north of the celestial equator go from 0° at the equator to +90° at the north celestial pole. Declinations south of the equator go from 0° to −90° at the south celestial pole.

Celestial longitude

The longitude of a point on Earth is the angular distance measured east along the Equator from the meridian passing through Greenwich, in England, to the meridian passing through the point. Like latitude, it is measured in degrees and minutes.

Celestial longitude, or right ascension (RA), is also an angular distance measured along the celestial equator. The starting point for measuring right ascension is the First Point in Aries, the point where the ecliptic crosses the celestial equator on March 21, the spring equinox.

So the right ascension of a star is the angular distance measured east from the First Point in Aries to the great circle passing through the star. It is not measured in degrees, however. It is measured in units of sidereal time. The reasoning behind this is that the celestial sphere rotates once every 24 sidereal hours, therefore 24 hours is equivalent to one complete circle of 360 degrees. One hour is equivalent to 15 degrees. Or in other words, the celestial sphere turns round 15 degrees in one hour.

This all sounds rather complicated, but this is more because of the terminology rather than the concept. If you can map-read on Earth using latitude and longitude, you will soon get the hang of map-reading on the celestial sphere using declination and right ascension.

Planispheres

A useful device to carry with you when star-gazing is a planisphere. This provides a quick and convenient way of finding and identifying the stars visible on any date and at any time of the night. Since the stars you see depend on your location on Earth, different planispheres are available for different latitudes.

A planisphere consists of two parts, a base and a movable disc that can rotate over the base. The base carries a map of all the stars visible from the given latitude on Earth during the year. A scale of months and days is marked around the edge. The movable disc has a window that reveals the stars visible above the horizon at a particular time. A scale showing the time of day (local time) in hours is marked around the edge of the movable disc.

Matching the hour of observation with the date brings into the window the stars visible at that time.

▲ Star-gazing in a planetarium is a sure way of getting bitten by the astronomy bug. An ingenious dumbbell-like projector throws images of the night sky on the domed ceiling of the planetarium. It can display the stars and constellations visible from any latitude on Earth and at any time: in the present, past and even the future.

▶ Planispheres for Earth latitudes 42° North (top) and 35° South. The former is suitable for most of the USA and southern Europe; the latter for Australia and New Zealand. Note that the scales on these two planispheres go in opposite directions. This is because the northern planisphere is centred on the northern celestial pole, and the southern one is centred on the southern celestial pole. So looking towards the poles, the sky appears to rotate in opposite directions.

◀ This magnificent vista of stars
and glowing gas is located in the
southern constellation Carina.
The gas cloud surrounds the
giant variable star Eta Carinae,
and is known as the Eta Carinae
Nebula (NGC3372). It is
divided by dark lanes of dust.

2

MAPPING THE STARS

As you saw in the first chapter, different constellations come into view season by season as the Earth makes its annual journey around the Sun. This chapter takes a closer look at the constellations as, month by month, they take it in turns to occupy centre stage in the late evening skies.

Views of the night sky over the year are presented as a series of monthly maps, from January to December. These maps represent segments of the celestial sphere. Each map shows all the constellations visible in that segment at that particular time. But which constellations an observer will see depends on the observer's latitude, or precise location on Earth. An observer in Australia, in the Southern Hemisphere, will not be able to see some of the far northern constellations that an observer in Canada will see, and vice versa.

Two additional star maps are centred on the celestial poles, representing the "top" and "bottom" of the celestial sphere. To far northern and far southern observers, part of these regions of the sky will always be visible throughout the year.

THE MONTHLY MAPS

Fourteen star maps appear in this chapter – one for each month of the year, plus one each for the north and south polar regions. Together, the maps cover the whole of the celestial sphere, with plenty of overlap. As with all maps, there is a certain amount of distortion, for they are representing a curved surface on flat paper.

▼ The European astronomy satellite Hipparchos (high-precision parallax collecting satellite), which has established the positions of more than 120,000 stars with unprecedented accuracy. It has brought a new dimension to astrometry, or positional astronomy.

The maps are drawn with a grid of celestial latitude and longitude, or "declination" and "right ascension". Declination is measured in degrees north (+) or south (−) of the celestial equator; right ascension is measured in hours and minutes of sidereal time. This grid provides a reference for locating stars on the celestial sphere. It can be used to locate other stars that are not included on these maps.

These maps feature stars down to the fifth magnitude, slightly above naked-eye visibility. Stars fainter than this are shown if they are of particular interest.

The stars are labelled with letters of the Greek alphabet according to the Bayer system, in which α (alpha) is the brightest in the constellation, β (beta) the next brightest, and so on. Mostly on these maps, only the stars featured in the text are labelled, making them easier to locate. In the text the letters are spelled out, as in Alpha Centauri. As an *aide memoire* the complete Greek alphabet is given in the table below.

Many of the brightest stars also have a proper name, such as Sirius for Alpha Canis Majoris. Proper names are given for the best known of these.

Some variable stars are identified by their Bayer letter, but others are identified according to a different system. The first variable discovered in a constellation is denoted R, the next S, and so on. After Z, the variables become RR, RS, and so on. On the maps, two symbols are used for variables: ◉ for variables that remain visible to the naked eye at minimum, and ○ for variables that fall below naked-eye visibility.

Deep-sky objects

By this we mean nebulae, open clusters, globular clusters and galaxies. These are marked on the maps with their own symbols, and they are usually identified either by an M number or just by a number.

The M number is the Messier number, or the number assigned to the particular object in a catalogue of more than 100 nebulous objects drawn up by the French astronomer Charles Messier in the 18th century. M42 in Orion is the Orion Nebula. Messier was an ardent comet-hunter, and drew up his catalogue pin-pointing nebulae and clusters that might be confused with new comets.

A number by itself next to a deep-sky object symbol denotes the NGC number of the object. This is the number in the *New General Catalogue of Nebulae and Clusters of Stars* compiled by the Danish astronomer Johann Dreyer and first published in 1888. The Messier numbers also have their equivalent NGC numbers: M42, for example, is NGC1976. But on the maps we show only the Messier number.

▶ Stars pack together densely in the Milky Way, as here in Monoceros. The rose-petal form of the cloud of glowing gas we see here earns it the name of the Rosette Nebula. The open star cluster at its centre is NGC2244, easily seen in binoculars.

This diagram shows how the monthly star maps that follow relate to the celestial sphere. The celestial sphere is shown "exploded" into 12 segments – one for each month of the year.

Each segment covers two hours of Right Ascension. It forms the central part of one of the monthly maps (see right). The stars, of course, appear on the inner surface of the segment.

The north polar and south polar star maps are derived from the northern and southern "caps" of the celestial sphere, centred on the celestial poles.

North celestial pole

North polar map

Monthly maps

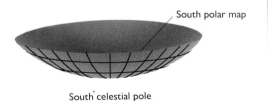

South polar map

South celestial pole

THE GREEK ALPHABET

α Alpha	ι Iota	ρ Rho
β Beta	κ Kappa	σ Sigma
γ Gamma	λ Lambda	τ Tau
δ Delta	μ Mu	υ Upsilon
ε Epsilon	ν Nu	φ Phi
ζ Zeta	ξ Xi	χ Chi
η Eta	ο Omicron	ψ Psi
θ Theta	π Pi	ω Omega

▼ This is a smaller version of one of the monthly maps (October), with annotations to point out salient features.

Ⓐ
This lighter area shows the position of the Milky Way.

Ⓑ
Symbol for a planetary nebula. The number is its NGC number.

Ⓒ
Symbol for an open cluster. The number is its NGC number.

Ⓓ
Symbol for a galaxy. The M number is its number in the Messier catalogue.

Ⓔ
This dashed line shows the ecliptic, the apparent path of the Sun across the celestial sphere.

Ⓕ
The line of zero declination, marking the celestial equator.

Ⓖ
The Greek letter Beta is the Bayer letter, which indicates that this star is the second brightest in the constellation.

Ⓗ
Star name. Some of the best-known stars are labelled with their name as well as their Bayer letter.

▶ Also included on each spread with the monthly star map are two "sky views" like this. One shows what an observer in mid-latitudes in the Northern Hemisphere would see looking south at about 11 pm local time in the first week of the month. The other shows what an observer in the Southern Hemisphere would see looking north at the same time.

Ⓘ
Name of the constellation in Latin.

Ⓙ
Scale of declination, or celestial latitude. The minus sign applies in the southern hemisphere.

Ⓚ
Scale of right ascension, or celestial longitude.

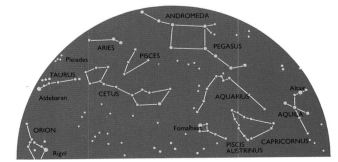

NORTH POLAR STARS

The north polar region is centred on Polaris, the Pole Star, which moves scarcely at all in the sky. Ursa Major is the outstanding constellation and is circumpolar – always visible – to observers north of latitude 40°.

▲ Stars trail around the north celestial pole in this long-exposure photograph taken with an ordinary tripod-mounted camera. The short arc at the centre was made by Polaris, which is less than one degree away from the pole.

Andromeda *See page 78.*

Auriga, the Charioteer *See page 44.*

Boötes, the Herdsman *See page 52.*

Cassiopeia *See page 80.*

Cepheus
This is quite a faint constellation, probably best found by using Alpha and Beta Cassiopeiae as pointers. By far the most spectacular star in the constellation is Mu, which William Herschel dubbed the Garnet Star. It is noticeably red even to the naked eye and looks really beautiful in binoculars. Mu is a variable star of the Mira type, varying between about magnitudes 3.5 and 5 over about two years.

Another interesting star is Delta, also a variable. It varies with absolute precision between magnitudes 3.5 and 4.4 in 5.4 days. It is the prototype star of the regular-as-clockwork variables known as the Cepheids. Delta is also a double star, with a bluish companion.

Cygnus, the Swan *See page 84.*

Draco, the Dragon
This sprawling constellation winds nearly halfway around the north celestial pole. Interestingly, Alpha, also called Thuban, used to be the Pole Star about 4,500 years ago. A passage in the Great Pyramid of Giza, constructed at about that time, was aligned on the star. The location of the celestial poles changes slowly because of precession, a kind of wobbling of the Earth's axis.

Among the several fine double stars in Draco is Nu, a pair of white stars of identical brightness. Eta, Psi and Xi are also double. Enclosed by the "neck" of the Dragon is one of the finest planetary nebulae in the heavens, 37 Draconis (NGC6543). It presents a noticeably blue disc, although the central star is difficult to make out.

Hercules *See page 54.*

Lacerta, the Lizard *See page 61.*

Lynx, the Lynx *See page 49.*

Perseus *See page 67.*

Ursa Major, the Great Bear *See page 94.*

Ursa Minor, the Little Bear
Also called the Little Dipper, this constellation is best known because its brightest star, Polaris, is less than one degree away from the north celestial pole. Polaris, also called the Pole Star and the North Star, is not especially bright, and is best found by using Merak and Dubhe in Ursa Major as pointers.

Polaris is a second-magnitude star, and is actually a Cepheid variable, although the change of brightness is not really noticeable. It is also a double star, with a faint (magnitude 9) bluish companion.

Beta, also called Kocab, has about the same brightness as Polaris and is sometimes confused with it, but it is noticeably more orange.

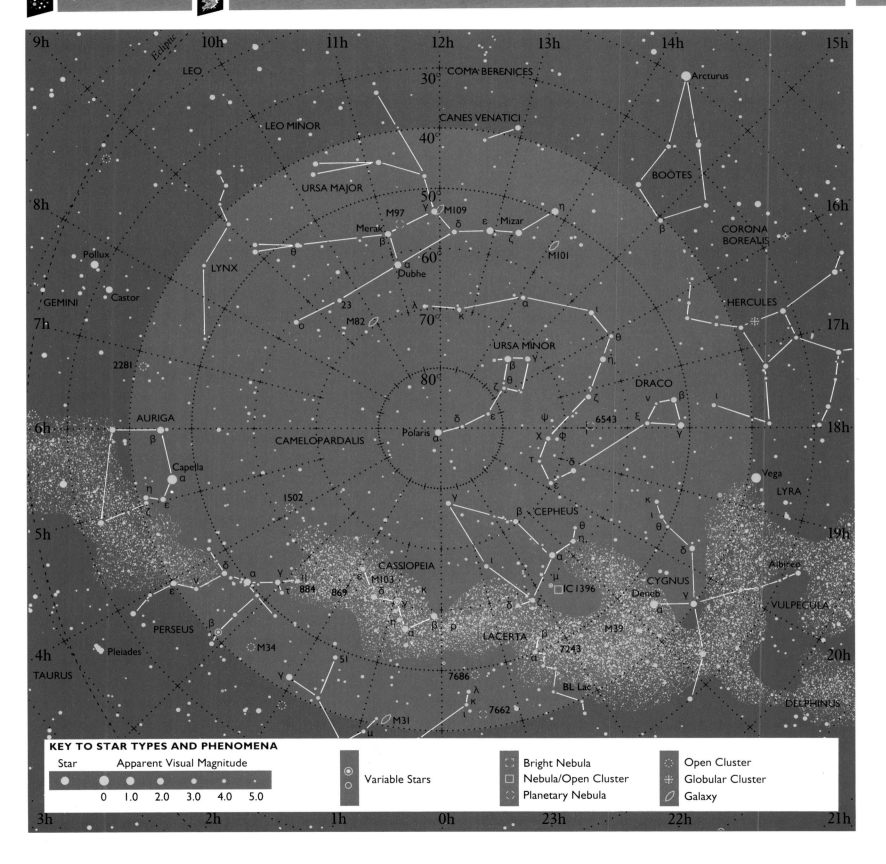

KEY TO STAR TYPES AND PHENOMENA

Star   Apparent Visual Magnitude

0 1.0 2.0 3.0 4.0 5.0

Variable Stars

Bright Nebula
Nebula/Open Cluster
Planetary Nebula

Open Cluster
Globular Cluster
Galaxy

SOUTH POLAR STARS

The south polar region might lack a convenient pole star, but it is richly endowed with brilliant objects. The Milky Way here is dazzling, and contains the unmistakable Southern Cross and its pointers, Alpha and Beta Centauri.

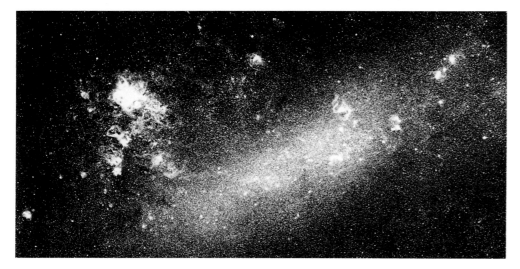

▲ This is the largest of the two Magellanic Clouds that are a feature of far southern skies. Located in Dorado, it is a rather shapeless mass of stars about 30,000 light years across. The Small Magellanic Cloud, in Tucana, lies about 20,000 light years farther away and is about 16,000 light years across.

Ara, the Altar

This constellation lies mainly in the Milky Way, and is a good region for sweeping with binoculars. Among its fine globular clusters is NGC6397, one of the closest known. It is found roughly midway between Beta and Theta.

NGC6193, roughly on a line from Theta through Alpha, is the brightest of the open clusters in the constellation and is embedded in nebulosity.

Carina, the Keel

A fine constellation of bright stars, nebulae and clusters, set in the Milky Way. Its leading star, Canopus, shines like a beacon even in this rich region of the heavens. At magnitude −0.7, it is the second brightest star in the night sky, after Sirius.

From Canopus, Carina extends nearly to Crux. Its stars Iota and Epsilon form, with Delta and Kappa Velae, the so-called False Cross. This is sometimes mistaken for the true Southern Cross of Crux.

Eta is one of the more interesting stars, not particularly bright at present, but once as bright as Canopus. It is embedded in one of the most glorious nebulae in the heavens, the Eta Carinae Nebula (NGC3372), which is visible to the naked eye and splendid in binoculars.

Close to Epsilon is the fine open cluster NGC2516, another naked-eye subject. Bluish white Theta is sur-

rounded by the bright open cluster IC2602. The open cluster NGC3114 and the globular cluster NGC2808 are among other objects well worth looking at in this stunning constellation.

Centaurus, the Centaur *See page 82.*

Crux, the Southern Cross *See page 82.*

Dorado, the Swordfish

Dorado is a mainly undistinguished constellation. Among the few bright stars, Beta is a Cepheid variable, and one of the brightest known. Dorado is notable mainly because it contains most of the Large Magellanic Cloud (LMC).

The LMC is the nearest galaxy to our own, and is clearly visible to the naked eye as a hazy patch of light. It looks beautiful in binoculars and a small telescope, which will resolve some of the brightest stars and nebulae.

One of the nebulae, however, can be seen even with the naked eye. It is the Tarantula Nebula (NGC2070, also called 30 Doradus). It was in this nebula that the spectacular supernova SN1987A exploded in February 1987, the most spectacular for centuries.

Eridanus *See page 66.*

Grus, the Crane *See page 60.*

Lupus, the Wolf *See page 53.*

Puppis, the Poop *See page 47.*

Tucana, the Toucan

Although its stars are quite faint, Tucana has two claims to fame. It includes the Small Magellanic Cloud (SMC) and one of the two finest globular clusters in the heavens, 47 Tucanae.

The SMC is a neighbouring galaxy, a little farther away than the LMC in Dorado and not so spectacular to look at. Nevertheless, even a small telescope will bring into focus nebulae and clusters and even individual stars.

The globular cluster 47 Tucanae (NGC104) lies on the edge of the SMC and vies with Omega Centauri in Centaurus in splendour. It is easily visible to the naked eye and brilliant in binoculars. Another globular cluster, NGC362, lies close by, again right on the edge of the SMC.

Sagittarius, the Archer *See page 88*

Vela, the Sails *See page 49.*

KEY TO STAR TYPES AND PHENOMENA

Star   Apparent Visual Magnitude

0   1.0   2.0   3.0   4.0   5.0

⊚ ○ Variable Stars

⬚ Bright Nebula
▢ Nebula/Open Cluster
◇ Planetary Nebula

⠂ Open Cluster
✳ Globular Cluster
⬭ Galaxy

January Stars

*The hexagonal pattern formed by six bright stars –
Sirius, Rigel, Aldebaran, Capella, Pollux and
Procyon – spans the meridian – the north-south line.
Right on the meridian is a seventh bright star, the
reddish Betelgeux.*

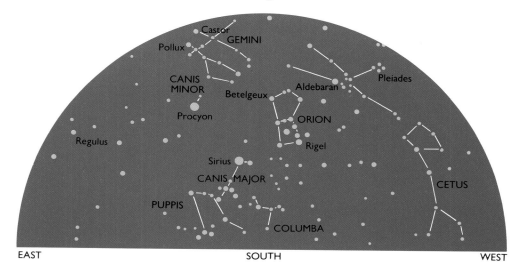

EAST   SOUTH   WEST

▲ **Northern Hemisphere
View of the night sky in
mid-latitudes looking
south at about 11 pm local
time on about January 7.**
Orion in mid-sky acts as a
signpost to super-bright Sirius
in the south-east and to the
noticeably orange Aldebaran
in the north-west.

▼ **Southern Hemisphere
View of the night sky in
Australia and southern
Africa looking north at
about 11 pm local time on
about January 7.**
In this aspect, the hexagon of
stars appears a perfect shape
and right in the centre of the
sky. It is spectacular.

WEST   NORTH   EAST

Auriga, the Charioteer

This conspicuous kite-shaped constellation lies astride
the Milky Way. It can be quickly located by its leading
star, Capella, the sixth brightest star in the sky. Close to
Capella is a triangle of fainter stars, known as the Haedi,
or the Kids. Of the three, Epsilon and Zeta are the most
interesting: they are both eclipsing binaries.

The Epsilon system consists of a yellow supergiant
and a huge dark companion star we cannot see. Usually at
about magnitude 3, it dims to magnitude 4 every 27 years
when the dark companion eclipses the bright star. In the
more colourful Zeta system, the components are an
orange supergiant and a smaller blue star. The change in
brightness, every 2 years 8 months, is not easy to detect.

Auriga also contains three bright open clusters, M36,
M37 and M38, easily seen in binoculars. They lie in a
more or less straight line at the edge of the Milky Way
between Theta Aurigae and Beta Tauri in the adjoining
constellation.

Canis Major, the Great Dog

Although only a small constellation, Canis Major boasts
the brightest star in the sky, Sirius (magnitude −1.5),
also called the Dog Star. As stars go, pure white Sirius is
not truly very bright. It appears so bright because it is
relatively close to Earth, less than nine light years away.
This is scarcely a stone's throw as far as distances in the
Universe are concerned.

Sirius is a binary star with a small but dense companion.
This Companion of Sirius (nicknamed appropriately the
Pup) is a white dwarf, and indeed the first of this type of
star to be discovered, in 1862. Although it is magnitude
8, the Pup is difficult to see because it orbits close to
Sirius and tends to be obscured by that star's glare.

Of the other bright stars in Canis Major, the brightest
is Epsilon. It is actually tens of thousands of times more
luminous than Sirius, but lies a hundred times farther away.

Among several open clusters in Canis Major, M41 is
the brightest. Located just south of Sirius, it may in good
viewing conditions be visible to the naked eye as a misty
glow. Small telescopes show up to two dozen bright stars
from the total of about 100.

Another striking open cluster is NGC2362, gathered
around the fourth-magnitude Tau. It contains about 40
very young stars. In binoculars, the whole of this southern
part of the constellation makes spectacular sweeping
since it lies in the Milky Way.

Canis Minor, the Little Dog *See page 46.*

Carina, the Keel *See page 42.*

Columba, the Dove

This constellation has relatively faint stars, but is easily found because it lies in an unusually bare region of the southern skies. It contains a number of globular clusters and galaxies, but only the cluster NGC1851 is visible in small telescopes.

Eridanus *See page 66.*

Gemini, the Twins *See page 46.*

Lepus, the Hare

This constellation lies immediately south of Orion and is thus easy to locate. It is small but contains some interesting objects. They include R Leporis, found by continuing a line through Alpha and Mu. It is a Mira variable star with a wide variation in brightness, between about magnitudes 5 and 10 over a period of about 14 months. It is one of the reddest stars we know, and is sometimes called the Crimson Star.

Gamma is an interesting double star, with orange and yellow components. Equidistant from Gamma and Epsilon and in line with Alpha and Beta is the globular cluster M79. It is small but bright.

Lynx, the Lynx *See page 49.*

Monoceros, the Unicorn *See page 47.*

Orion *See page 86.*

Perseus *See page 67.*

Puppis, the Poop *See page 47.*

Taurus, the Bull *See page 92.*

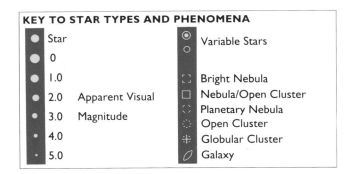

KEY TO STAR TYPES AND PHENOMENA

Star		
0		Variable Stars
1.0		
2.0	Apparent Visual	Bright Nebula
3.0	Magnitude	Nebula/Open Cluster
		Planetary Nebula
4.0		Open Cluster
5.0		Globular Cluster
		Galaxy

FEBRUARY STARS

The panoply of brilliant stars astride and to the west of the Milky Way has moved from centre stage, but is still stunning in the west. However, east of the Milky Way the skies appear rather dull by comparison.

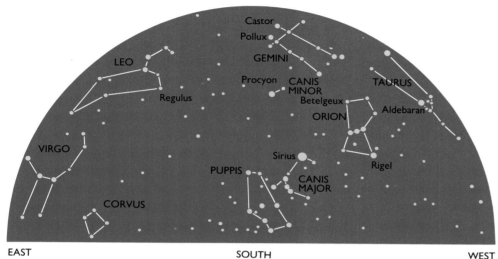

EAST   SOUTH   WEST

▲ Northern Hemisphere View of the night sky in mid-latitudes looking south at about 11 pm local time on about February 7.
The bright stars in mid-sky line up more or less parallel with the horizon. From the east, they are Regulus, Procyon, Betelgeux and Aldebaran.

▼ Southern Hemisphere View of the night sky in Australia and southern Africa looking north at about 11 pm local time on about February 7.
The hexagonal arrangement of bright stars has slipped west, with Capella barely visible. In the east, Leo is ascending.

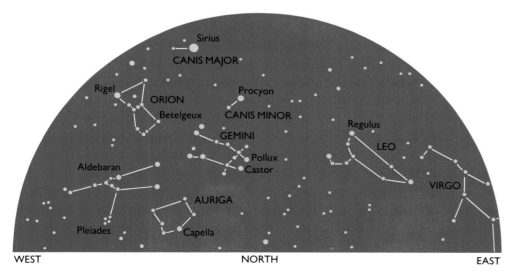

WEST   NORTH   EAST

Auriga, the Charioteer *See page 44.*

Cancer, the Crab
Sandwiched between Leo and Gemini, Cancer is one of the constellations of the zodiac. Though relatively faint, it contains much of interest. In the middle of the constellation is the beautiful open cluster M44, called Praesepe, or the Beehive. It is one of the most prominent clusters, easily visible to the naked eye. Binoculars show up dozens of its stars; while large telescopes reveal hundreds.

Close to Alpha is another open cluster, M67, visible in binoculars but needing a telescope to bring out individual stars. Cancer also features two lovely double stars, Iota and Zeta. Both have yellow and blue components.

Canis Major, the Great Dog *See page 44.*

Canis Minor, the Little Dog
Little by name and little in size, this constellation is notable for its one bright star, Procyon. At a distance of about 11 light years, Procyon is the third closest bright star to Earth, after Alpha Centauri and Sirius. And like Sirius, it has a faint white dwarf companion.

Carina, the Keel *See page 42.*

Columba, the Dove *See page 45.*

Gemini, the Twins
This splendid constellation of the zodiac is well named for it boasts twin first-magnitude stars, Castor and Pollux. Pollux is the brighter of the two and is the more colourful, being a rich yellow-orange.

Castor, however, is the more interesting twin because it is a multiple star system. A small telescope resolves Castor into two components, and brings a fainter third into view. The spectra of the three stars reveal that each is a spectroscopic binary, with a close companion, making a six-star system in all.

Among Gemini's double stars is Zeta. Its brightest component is a Cepheid variable, which fluctuates in brightness over a period of ten days. The change in brightness can be seen by comparison with the steady shining Delta, which a small telescope will reveal to be a double.

A good binocular subject in the constellation is M35, a large and bright open cluster just north of Mu and Eta. Telescopes will reveal close to Delta the greenish disc of NGC2392, a fine planetary nebula.

Hydra, the Water Snake *See pages 48 and 50.*

Leo, the Lion *See page 48.*

Lepus, the Hare *See page 45.*

Lynx, the Lynx *See page 49.*

Monoceros, the Unicorn

A faint constellation, Monoceros is located between the two "Dogs", Canis Minor and Major. It has no bright stars, but spans a particularly rich area of the Milky Way.

Beta is one of the most interesting stars. It is a multiple star, whose three components can be seen as a neat triangle even in small telescopes.

Close by Epsilon is a striking open cluster, NGC2244. Large telescopes show it to be surrounded by one of the most beautiful nebulae in the heavens, the flower-like Rosette Nebula (NGC2237). Another nebula, the Cone Nebula, surrounds the open cluster NGC2264, just south of Chi Geminorum. Midway between Alpha and Beta is another open cluster, M50.

Puppis, the Poop

Puppis is a fine southern constellation nestling in the Milky Way. It abounds in rich star fields and clusters. The second-magnitude Zeta is the brightest star. Electric blue in colour, it is one of the hottest stars known, with a surface temperature of tens of thousands of degrees.

Numerous doubles dotted around the constellation include Kappa and Sigma. Pi is one of a quartet of stars, well seen in a small telescope. Close to Sigma is L^2, a long-period variable that changes noticeably in brightness from magnitudes 3 to 6 over a period of about five months.

Among the many open clusters are the naked-eye M47 and the fainter M46, which are located side by side and close to NGC2423. M93 is farther south, near Xi. Close to Zeta is NGC2477 containing hundreds of faint stars so densely packed that it almost looks like a globular cluster.

Ursa Major, the Great Bear *See page 94.*

Vela, the Sails *See page 49.*

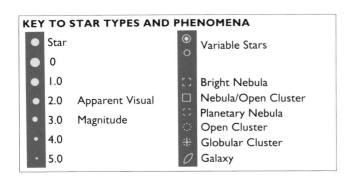

KEY TO STAR TYPES AND PHENOMENA

Star		Variable Stars
0		
1.0		Bright Nebula
2.0 Apparent Visual		Nebula/Open Cluster
3.0 Magnitude		Planetary Nebula
		Open Cluster
4.0		Globular Cluster
5.0		Galaxy

MARCH STARS

While Orion takes its curtain call in the west, the majestic Leo, with its distinctive "Sickle" head, occupies the mid-sky. Its presence heralds the onset of spring in the Northern Hemisphere and of autumn in the Southern.

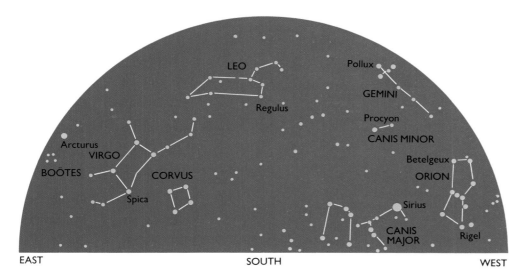

EAST   SOUTH   WEST

▲ **Northern Hemisphere View of the night sky in mid-latitudes looking south at about 11 pm local time on about March 7.**
Rigel is close to setting in the west. Sirius is also low down and about to make its exit. In the east, Spica is making its entrance.

▼ **Southern Hemisphere View of the night sky in Australia and southern Africa looking north at about 11 pm local time on about March 7.**
Regulus appears due north in the mid-sky. Spica and Arcturus appear in the east, the one vertically above the other.

WEST   NORTH   EAST

Cancer, the Crab *See page 46.*

Gemini, the Twins *See page 46.*

Hydra, the Water Snake (head)

Hydra winds its way, serpent-like, more than a quarter of the way around the celestial sphere. Indeed, it is the largest of all the constellations. It rears its head near Canis Minor, just north of the celestial equator, while its tail extends as far as Libra.

The only bright star in Hydra, the second-magnitude Alpha, is called Alphard, meaning the "Solitary One" because it is the only reasonably bright star in a barren region of the heavens. It is also known as Cor Hydrae, or the Hydra's Heart.

The stars in the Hydra's head make an attractive group in low-powered binoculars. One of them, Epsilon, is a colourful double, separated in larger telescopes. M48 is a bright cluster approaching naked-eye visibility, found by moving southwards from the head past the close trio of stars, c.

The brightest planetary nebula in the heavens, NGC3242, lies in Hydra, just south of Mu. Small telescopes show this magnitude 9 object as a faint bluish green disc. Sometimes called the Ghost of Jupiter Nebula, its central star is clearly seen. (For Hydra's tail, see page 50.)

Leo, the Lion

This constellation of the zodiac is one that looks passably like the animal it is supposed to represent. The most recognizable shape in Leo is the Sickle, the sickle-like arrangement of stars that forms the lion's head and mane.

In the Sickle, Gamma, Mu and Lambda are all orange in colour. Gamma, often called Algeiba, the Lion's Mane, is a double, which can be resolved in a telescope into a pair of golden yellow stars.

Brighter than the Sickle stars is the first-magnitude Regulus, also called Cor Leonis, or the Lion's Heart. It is a double, with the fainter star of the eighth magnitude.

The other prominent shape in Leo is at the tail end, where there is a triangle of bright stars. Of this trio Beta, also called Denebola, is the brightest at about magnitude 2.

Beginning just south of Delta is a region rich in galaxies. The brightest ones lie south of a line joining Beta and Regulus. South of Theta are M65 and M66, both about magnitude 9 and both visible in binoculars in good seeing conditions. Like our own Galaxy, they are spirals, although large telescopes are needed to bring out their spiral form.

About midway between them and Regulus is another pair of spiral galaxies, M95 and M96. All four galaxies lie about the same distance away from Earth, some 30 million light years.

Lynx, the Lynx

Said to be so named because you have to be lynx-eyed to spot it, this is a faint constellation in a relatively empty part of the northern heavens. The third-magnitude Alpha is distinctly red.

Monoceros, the Unicorn *See page 47.*

Puppis, the Poop *See page 47.*

Ursa Major, the Great Bear *See page 94.*

Vela, the Sails

Vela spans the Milky Way in the southern skies and, like the adjacent constellations Centaurus, Puppis and Carina, is rich in star fields and clusters. In the constellation, the Milky Way splits up because of distant obscuring dust clouds.

Kappa and Delta are second-magnitude stars which, along with Iota and Epsilon in Carina, form a noticeable cross-shape, the so-called False Cross. The False Cross has much the same orientation as the true cross of Crux close by, but is larger.

Immediately north of Delta is Omicron, which forms part of the cluster IC2391. Delta, Omicron and the rest of the cluster look great through binoculars. Another good binocular subject is NGC2547, just south of Gamma.

Gamma is easy to spot as a double, and its blue-white brighter component is particularly hot and luminous. It is a type known as a Wolf-Rayet star, an unstable body thought to be on the brink of becoming a supernova and blasting itself apart.

South of Lambda, long-exposure photographs reveal wisps of an extensive nebula, known as the Gum Nebula (NGC2736). It is a supernova remnant, the gaseous remains of a supernova explosion that took place about 11,000 years ago.

KEY TO STAR TYPES AND PHENOMENA

Star	Variable Stars
0	
1.0	Bright Nebula
2.0 Apparent Visual	Nebula/Open Cluster
3.0 Magnitude	Planetary Nebula
4.0	Open Cluster
	Globular Cluster
5.0	Galaxy

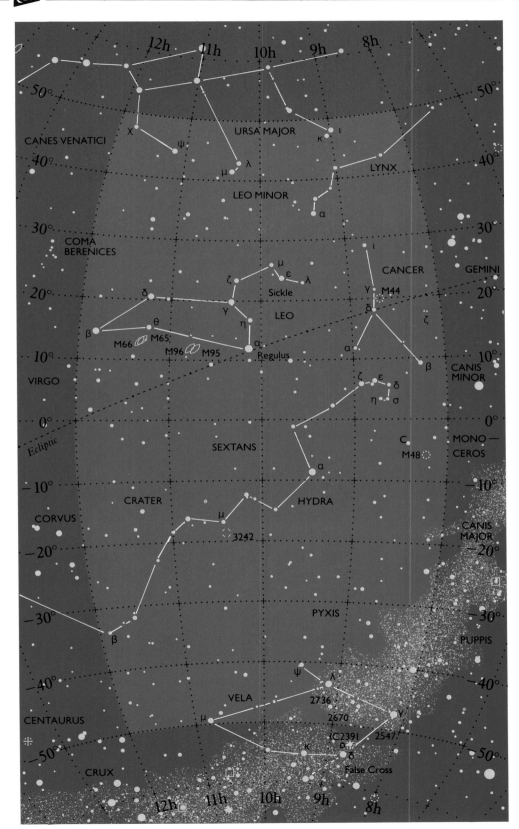

APRIL STARS

Leo is still prominent, but as a whole the sky looks bare because of the presence of the sprawling Hydra and Virgo. These, the two largest constellations in the heavens, have no very bright stars, except for Spica.

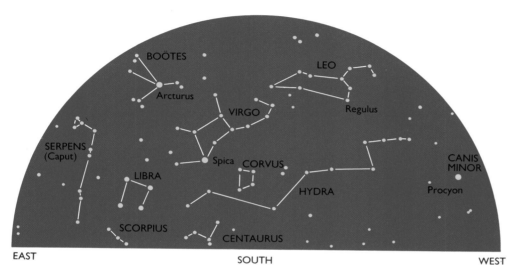

EAST   SOUTH   WEST

▲ **Northern Hemisphere View of the night sky in mid-latitudes looking south at about 11 pm local time on about April 7.**
High in the east Arcturus is the brightest star, forming an expansive triangle with Regulus and Spica. Procyon lies in the west.

▼ **Southern Hemisphere View of the night sky in Australia and southern Africa looking north at about 11 pm local time on about April 7.**
This is a good month to experience the extragalactic delights of the "empty" region between Leo and Boötes.

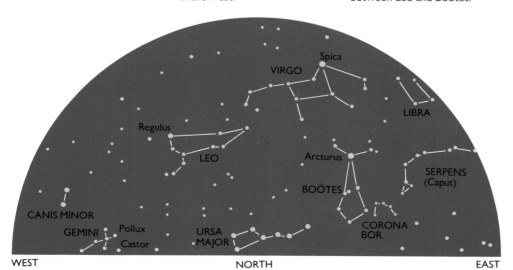

WEST   NORTH   EAST

Canes Venatici, the Hunting Dogs

Overall, this is a faint constellation, located underneath the handle of the Plough. However, it boasts one of the finest globular clusters in northern skies and one of the most distinctive galaxies.

Even its leading star, Alpha, is only slightly brighter than the third magnitude. It is also called Cor Caroli, meaning Charles's Heart, a name given to it by the second Astronomer Royal, Edmond Halley. The heart in question is that of the executed Charles I of England. Alpha is a double, which a small telescope will easily resolve.

The first of the telescopic highlights of Canes Venatici is the M3 globular cluster. It is located about halfway between Cor Caroli and the bright Arcturus in the neighbouring constellation Boötes. At about magnitude 6, it is on the limit of naked-eye visibility, and binoculars show it as a fuzzy patch. Telescopes will resolve it into an enormous globe of closely packed stars.

The other telescopic highlight of the constellation is M51, the famous Whirlpool Galaxy. Small telescopes show it as a pair of hazy spots. Larger instruments bring out its classic face-on spiral shape. The two spots in fact turn out to be the centres of two connected galaxies. Historically, the Whirlpool is important because it was the first galaxy to have its spiral structure resolved.

Like the neighbouring constellation Coma Berenices, Canes Venatici is richly endowed with galaxies. Among the brighter ones worth looking for are M63, M94 and M106. M63 is located just north of 20 Canes Venatici; M94, just over halfway from 20 to Beta; and M106, from Beta about halfway to Gamma Ursa Majoris. Larger telescopes will reveal a string of fainter galaxies going south from M106.

Centaurus, the Centaur *See page 82.*

Coma Berenices, Berenice's Hair *See page 52.*

Corvus, the Crow

A tiny constellation on Hydra's back, easy to spot because of its quartet of leading stars, all of (or slightly below) third magnitude. They make a nice group in binoculars. Delta is an easy double, with components of contrasting colours.

Hydra, the Water Snake (tail)

Hydra continues to wind through this segment of the celestial sphere. Among viewable objects in this, the tail end of the water snake, is the star R, located near Gamma. It is a Mira variable star, distinctly red. It varies markedly in brightness between magnitudes 4 and 11 over a period of just over a year.

Due south of R, on the edge of the constellation, is one of the brightest face-on spiral galaxies in the heavens, M83. Larger instruments reveal it is a barred spiral galaxy, with a distinct bar across the middle.

Leo, the Lion *See page 48.*

Ursa Major, the Great Bear *See page 94.*

Vela, the Sails *See page 49.*

Virgo, the Virgin *See page 96.*

▼ One of the most distinctive objects in the heavens, the Whirlpool Galaxy (M51). It is actually two connected galaxies. The main spiral is noted for its bright nucleus and well-defined arms.

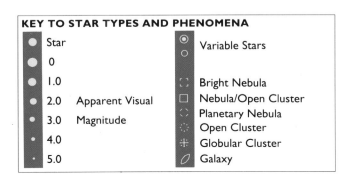

KEY TO STAR TYPES AND PHENOMENA

Star		Variable Stars
0		
1.0		Bright Nebula
2.0	Apparent Visual	Nebula/Open Cluster
3.0	Magnitude	Planetary Nebula
		Open Cluster
4.0		Globular Cluster
5.0		Galaxy

MAY STARS

Arcturus and Spica are close to the meridian this month, and provide a pleasing colour contrast. Arcturus is a lovely orange, while Spica is pure white. Both are giants, the one cool, the other very hot.

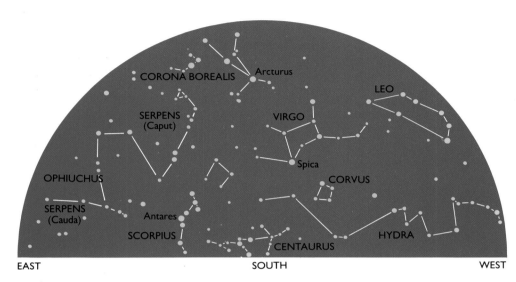

EAST | SOUTH | WEST

▲ **Northern Hemisphere View of the night sky in mid-latitudes looking south at about 11 pm local time on about May 7.** Coloured Arcturus has a rival appearing over the horizon, red Antares. The whole of Serpens – Caput and Cauda – is now visible in the east.

▼ **Southern Hemisphere View of the night sky in Australia and southern Africa looking north at about 11 pm local time on about May 7.** Leo is slipping towards the horizon. At lower latitudes, the Plough may just be glimpsed on the horizon.

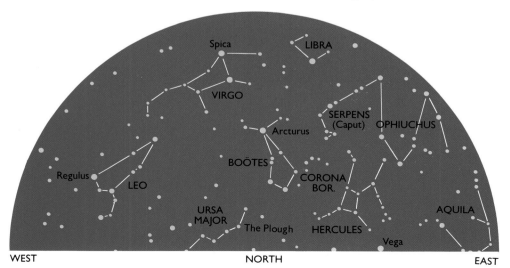

WEST | NORTH | EAST

Boötes, the Herdsman

This fine kite-shaped constellation boasts the brightest star in northern skies and the fourth brightest star in the whole heavens. This star is Arcturus ("Bear-keeper"). It is a red giant, which explains its noticeable orange colour. It can perhaps best be found by following round the curve of the handle of the Plough.

There are several doubles of note in Boötes, none finer than Epsilon. The star appears only slightly coloured in binoculars, but a telescope separates it into beautiful yellowish orange and bluish green components, making it one of the most attractive doubles in the heavens.

Xi is another colourful double, which even small telescopes should be able to separate into a yellow and orange pair. The third fine double in the constellation is Mu. Binoculars will separate it into two yellow stars. A telescope will split the fainter of the two into a further yellow pair.

Boötes has few interesting deep-sky objects, such as galaxies and clusters. There is, however, one reasonable globular cluster, NGC5466, which forms one corner of a parallelogram with Rho, Alpha and Eta.

Canes Venatici, the Hunting Dogs *See page 50.*

Centaurus, the Centaur *See page 82.*

Coma Berenices, Berenice's Hair

Like Canes Venatici to the north, Coma Berenices is faint and inconspicuous at first sight, but look at it in binoculars, small and large telescopes, and it becomes increasingly richer with every increase in magnification.

Essentially, it is a constellation dominated by galaxies. Literally hundreds of them lie in this region of the heavens, forming the so-called Coma Cluster. At a distance of some 450 million light years, these galaxies are mostly beyond the range of amateur telescopes. However, there are quite a few much closer galaxies, which are visible in small telescopes. M64 is one of them. It is located on a line joining Alpha and Gamma, near star 35. Large telescopes show it as an ellipse, with a distinctive dark spot. For this reason, it is known as the Black-Eye Galaxy.

Farther along the Alpha-to-Gamma line is the slightly fainter NGC4565, known as the Needle Galaxy. It appears needle-like because we are looking at it edge-on. The galaxies M85 and M100, both of the ninth magnitude, form part of a dense grouping of galaxies at the southern edge of the constellation, which continues into Virgo. This whole region is a fascinating one for the telescopic browser.

Corona Borealis, the Northern Crown *See page 54.*

Corvus, the Crow *See page 50.*

Hydra, the Water Snake *See pages 48 and 50.*

Libra, the Scales

Libra is a faint constellation of the zodiac, which lacks any really bright stars. It perhaps suffers from being cheek by jowl with the bright stars in the head of Scorpius.

Indeed, originally, the stars in Libra formed the claws of the Scorpion. Its leading star Alpha (magnitude 2.7) is named Zubenelgenubi, meaning the "southern claw". It is slightly less bright than Beta, the "northern claw" Zubenelchemale.

Alpha is a fine wide double star, which binoculars separate easily. If the dim component (fifth magnitude) were somewhat brighter, Alpha would just be separable with the naked eye.

Beta has an unusual greenish colour. Delta is an eclipsing binary, similar to Algol. Every 56 hours, the dim component passes in front of the bright one, and the brightness of the system dips briefly from the fourth to the sixth magnitude.

Lupus, the Wolf

This constellation is sandwiched between Scorpius and Centaurus on the edge of the Milky Way. It is therefore a rewarding region for sweeping with binoculars. There are several doubles worth looking at in the constellation, including Pi, Kappa and Eta.

As for clusters, there are many that can be found in larger telescopes. More modest instruments will be able to pick up the globular cluster NGC5986, close to Eta, and the open cluster NGC5822, close to Zeta.

Scorpius, the Scorpion *See page 90.*

Serpens Caput, the Serpent's Head *See page 55.*

Ursa Major, the Great Bear *See page 94.*

Virgo, the Virgin *See page 96.*

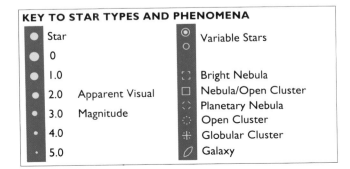

KEY TO STAR TYPES AND PHENOMENA

Star	Variable Stars
0	
1.0	Bright Nebula
2.0 Apparent Visual	Nebula/Open Cluster
3.0 Magnitude	Planetary Nebula
4.0	Open Cluster
5.0	Globular Cluster
	Galaxy

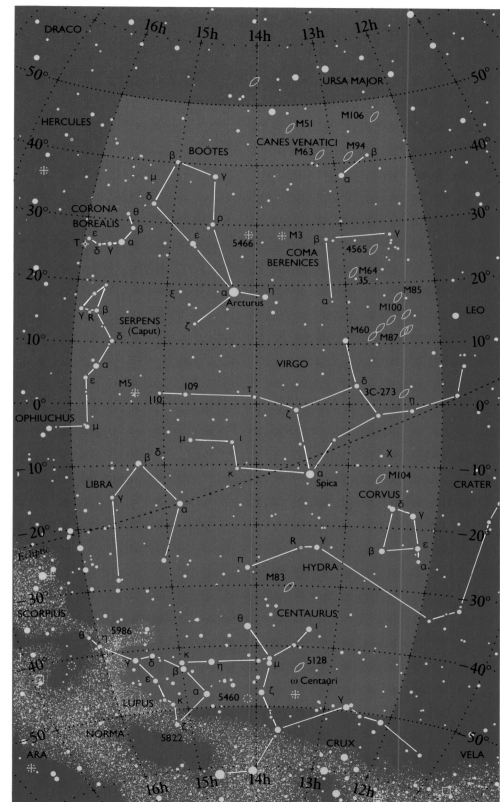

June Stars

In this month and July, Scorpius is a constellation to watch, low in northern skies and near the zenith in southern. Its brightest star, Antares, joins Arcturus, Vega, Deneb, Altair and Spica in the night sky starscape.

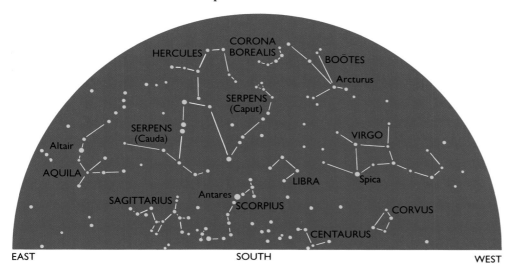

EAST   SOUTH   WEST

▲ **Northern Hemisphere View of the night sky in mid-latitudes looking south at about 11 pm local time on about June 7.**
The heads of the Serpent and the Scorpion lie due south. Compare the colours of Antares low down and Arcturus high up.

▼ **Southern Hemisphere View of the night sky in Australia and southern Africa looking north at about 11 pm local time on about June 7.**
This month provides a good opportunity for observing the northern constellations Boötes and Hercules.

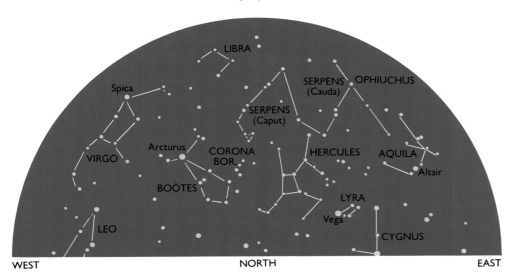

WEST   NORTH   EAST

Ara, the Altar *See page 42.*

Boötes, the Herdsman *See page 52.*

Centaurus, the Centaur *See page 82.*

Corona Borealis, the Northern Crown
This is a tiny, but easily recognizable constellation, a neat semicircle of stars with the second-magnitude Alpha in the middle of the arc. It contains a number of doubles, including Zeta and Nu, but is particularly notable for two remarkable variable stars.

One is R, located north of Delta in the "bowl". For most of the time R is about magnitude 6 and readily visible in binoculars, but from time to time it suddenly dims to about magnitude 12 or even lower. It may recover its brightness in a matter of months, but sometimes takes years. Astronomers think one explanation of the sudden dimming might be that the star periodically ejects clouds of sooty material, which blocks its light.

The other fascinating variable is T, located south of Epsilon. This star is usually only about magnitude 10, but sometimes flares up to brighter than 6 and becomes visible to the naked eye. Indeed, in 1866 and 1946, T became as bright as the second magnitude. Aptly called the Blaze Star, T periodically flares up in this way, over a matter of hours, because it is a type called a recurrent nova. No one knows when it may flare up again, so it is always worth watching.

Underneath the "bowl", beyond Beta, large telescopes will show one of the densest clusters of galaxies known, called Abell 2065. Over 400 galaxies are clustered closely together about 1,000 million light years away.

Draco, the Dragon *See page 40.*

Hercules
Hercules is a large constellation, in fact the fifth largest in the heavens. It is not overly impressive to the naked eye, but is richly endowed to the binocular and telescopic observer.

Its pièce de résistance is M13, the finest globular cluster in northern skies, just about visible to the naked eye on a really dark night. M13 is found on a line joining Zeta and Eta. Binoculars show it as a fuzzy blob, but telescopes resolve it into a conglomeration of countless stars.

M92 is another fine globular cluster, slightly fainter than M13, found on a line joining Eta with Iota. In larger telescopes NGC6210 is well worth observing. It is a small, bright planetary nebula with a brilliant blue central star.

Among the stars in Hercules, Alpha is noticeably red

and varies over a period of months between the third and fourth magnitudes. It is also a double star with reddish and greenish components. Delta, Rho and Mu are also doubles worth investigating.

Hydra, the Water Snake (tail) *See page 50.*

Libra, the Scales *See page 53.*

Lupus, the Wolf *See page 53.*

Lyra, the Lyre *See page 56.*

Ophiuchus, the Serpent-Bearer *See page 56.*

Sagittarius *See page 88.*

Scorpius, the Scorpion *See page 90.*

Serpens Caput, the Serpent's Head
This is the head part of Serpens, the Serpent, a constellation that is split into two by Ophiuchus, the Serpent-Bearer. The tail part is Serpens Cauda (see page 57). The triangle of stars in the Head look attractive in the same field in binoculars. Kappa and Rho to the north are distinctly reddish.

Also in the same field, close to Beta, is R, a Mira variable with a wide variation in brightness. At maximum, it reaches magnitude 6, but at minimum fades beyond the reach of binoculars. Its period is slightly less than a year. Delta and the orange Alpha are visible as doubles in a telescope.

However, the Head's most impressive object is the globular cluster M5, one of the finest of its type in northern skies. You can find it, close to the dim star 5, by continuing a line through Lambda and Alpha. It is also in line with the stars 110 and 109 Virginis in the neighbouring constellation Virgo.

Virgo, the Virgin *See page 96.*

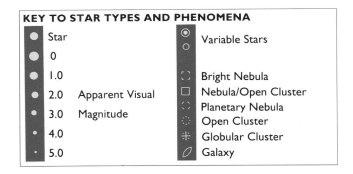

KEY TO STAR TYPES AND PHENOMENA

Star	
● 0	◉ Variable Stars
● 1.0	○
● 2.0 Apparent Visual	⬚ Bright Nebula
● 3.0 Magnitude	▢ Nebula/Open Cluster
● 4.0	◇ Planetary Nebula
· 5.0	⁛ Open Cluster
	✳ Globular Cluster
	⬭ Galaxy

July Stars

Vega is high in northern skies and low in southern. With Altair and Deneb, it makes up the Summer Triangle. The Milky Way, particularly the Sagittarius region, is now well placed for viewing in both hemispheres.

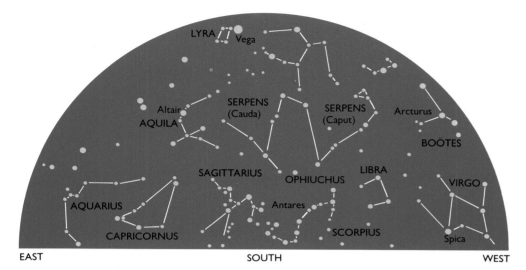

EAST SOUTH WEST

▲ **Northern Hemisphere View of the night sky in mid-latitudes looking south at about 11 pm local time on about July 7.** Sagittarius joins Scorpius near the southern horizon, offering northern observers a tantalizing glimpse of the delights of southern skies.

▼ **Southern Hemisphere View of the night sky in Australia and southern Africa looking north at about 11 pm local time on about July 7.** The Swan and the Eagle take wing along the Milky Way. The stars Deneb and Altair lie on a near-vertical line.

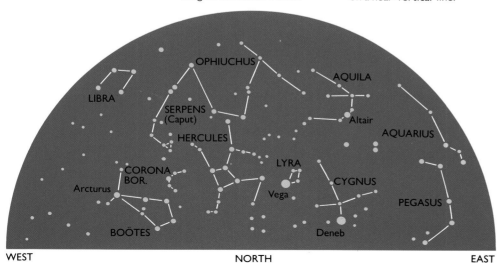

WEST NORTH EAST

Aquila, the Eagle *See page 58.*

Cygnus, the Swan *See page 84.*

Hercules *See page 54.*

Lyra, the Lyre
Although this is only a small constellation, it is packed with interesting objects, particularly a surfeit of fine double stars.

The only really bright star in Lyra is the first-magnitude Vega, sometimes called the Harp Star. The fifth brightest star in the heavens, it shines brilliantly in summer skies in the Northern Hemisphere, and is one of the trio of stars (along with Deneb in Cygnus and Altair in Aquila) that make up the Summer Triangle.

Close to Vega lies Epsilon, the well-known "double-double" star. It is so called because it is a double star easily visible in binoculars. And when its two components are observed in a small telescope, they are also seen to be double.

Immediately south of Vega, four stars form a parallelogram. Astronomically, the most interesting of them is Beta. First, Beta is a double star, with yellowish and bluish components. In addition, the brighter yellowish star is an eclipsing binary system. Its two stars are very close together, probably less than 35,000,000 kilometres (22,000,000 miles). Because of this, they are almost certainly egg-shaped, with gas streaming between them.

Beta changes from the third to the fourth magnitude every 13 days. And its variation can readily be followed using Delta or Zeta (both a steady magnitude 4.3) for comparison. Both these stars are also doubles, the Delta system easily being visible in binoculars.

Sandwiched between Beta and Gamma is one of the most striking of all heavenly objects, M57, the Ring Nebula, a colourful "smoke ring" puffed out by a dying star. It is not especially impressive in small telescopes, and requires long exposures in larger instruments to show its true splendour.

Ophiuchus, the Serpent-Bearer
This is a large constellation, which splits Serpens, the Serpent, into two – Caput (Head) and Cauda (Tail). In the south, it enters a particularly rich region of the Milky Way, where globular clusters abound.

Among these southern clusters is M19, found midway between Theta and Antares in the adjacent constellation Scorpius. Just north of Antares, on the Ophiuchus/Scorpius boundary, is the faint star Rho. It is worth scanning this region because it is occupied by extensive clouds of gas and dust. Even in binoculars you may be able to make out the dust lanes.

Two bright globular clusters, M10 and M12, lie in the relatively barren interior of Ophiuchus. M12 makes a triangle with Lambda and Delta, and M10 is close by.

Among the stars, 70 is a colourful orange and yellow double visible in telescopes. Close to star 66 is a faint (magnitude 9) red star called Barnard's Star. It is interesting for two related reasons. First, it is the nearest star to Earth after Proxima and Alpha Centauri, being only 5.9 light years away. Second, it is the star with the largest proper motion, or visible motion across the sky: over 10 seconds of arc per year.

Sagitta, the Arrow *See page 59.*

Sagittarius, the Archer *See page 88.*

Scorpius, the Scorpion *See page 90.*

Scutum, the Shield
Although it is a small constellation with no really bright stars, Scutum lies on the edge of a rich part of the Milky Way. It abounds in star clouds and dark nebulous regions.

The constellation's two highlights lie close together. Just south of Beta is R, a variable star that changes brightness irregularly between about the sixth and ninth magnitudes. Close by is a beautiful open cluster, M11, called the Wild Duck because its fan of stars is said to look like a duck in flight.

Serpens Cauda, the Serpent's Tail
This is the tail part of Serpens, a constellation split by Ophiuchus. The head part is Serpens Caput, see page 55. Perhaps the most interesting object in Serpens Cauda is M16, a scattered cluster of stars visible in binoculars quite close to Gamma Scuti in the adjacent constellation. Telescopes show the stars embedded in a glowing nebula, called the Eagle Nebula.

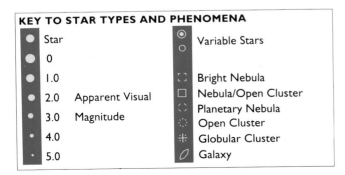

KEY TO STAR TYPES AND PHENOMENA

	Star		
	0		Variable Stars
	1.0		
	2.0 Apparent Visual		Bright Nebula
	3.0 Magnitude		Nebula/Open Cluster
			Planetary Nebula
	4.0		Open Cluster
	5.0		Globular Cluster
			Galaxy

August Stars

The Summer Triangle of the brilliant white Deneb, Vega and Altair spans the meridian, high in the sky in the Northern Hemisphere, low in the Southern. The appearance of Pegasus in the east, however, hints at a changing season.

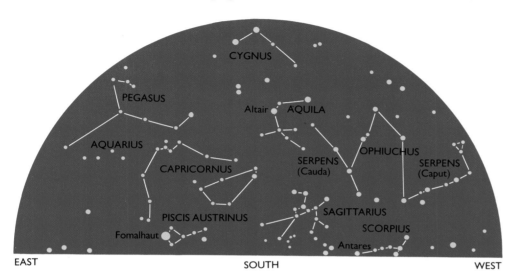

EAST   SOUTH   WEST

▲ **Northern Hemisphere View of the night sky in mid-latitudes looking south at about 11 pm local time on about August 7.** Part of Sagittarius is still visible this month; so, at lower latitudes, is Antares. But at higher latitudes, this star is just below the horizon.

▼ **Southern Hemisphere View of the night sky in Australia and southern Africa looking north at about 11 pm local time on about August 7.** Vega and Deneb are bright and prominent low down in the south, while Altair appears higher up.

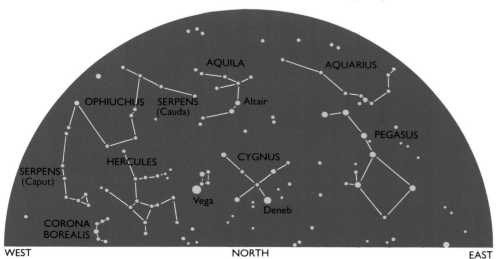

WEST   NORTH   EAST

Aquarius, the Water-Bearer *See page 60.*

Aquila, the Eagle
This is a fine constellation, whose curve of bright stars does rather resemble the wings of a bird in flight. Aquila straddles the Milky Way and the celestial equator, and contains rich star fields that are a delight to sweep with binoculars.

The brightest star, Altair, is one of the trio that form the prominent Summer Triangle. (The others are Deneb in Cygnus and Vega in Lyra.) Altair is a brilliant pure white star, contrasting nicely with one of its neighbours, the fainter Gamma, which is distinctly orange.

South of Altair is a noticeable line of three stars. Theta and Delta flank the central Eta, which is a Cepheid variable. It varies between the third and fourth magnitudes over about a week. Its progress can be followed by reference to the third-magnitude Theta and Delta and the fourth-magnitude Iota.

The curve of stars around Lambda acts as a good pointer to the Wild Duck cluster M11, in the neighbouring constellation Scutum.

Capricornus, the Sea Goat
Capricornus is one of the constellations of the zodiac, but is fairly inconspicuous. Its brightest stars, of about the third magnitude, form a pattern rather like a crooked triangle.

Alpha is a naked-eye double, but the two stars are not physically associated: the fainter one is more than ten times farther away than the brighter one. Both stars are themselves doubles. Beta is also double, and is a true binary star, whose components travel through space together.

The only noteworthy cluster in the constellation is M30, just outside the "crooked triangle" near Zeta. It is a globular cluster, visible in small telescopes but needing larger ones to resolve the stars properly.

Cygnus, the Swan *See page 84.*

Delphinus, the Dolphin
You can easily imagine this tiny constellation to be a leaping dolphin. Its bright stars form a group so compact that they almost look like an open cluster. In binoculars they all appear in the same field. In the main quadrilateral of stars, Gamma is a fine double, separated in small telescopes into golden yellow components.

Grus, the Crane *See page 60.*

Lacerta, the Lizard *See page 61.*

Lyra, the Lyre *See page 56.*

Sagitta, the Arrow

This is one of the smallest constellations in the heavens, but it has quite a distinctive, arrow-like shape. It lies within the Milky Way, almost due north of the bright stars in Aquila.

To the naked eye, Sagitta appears a rather bland region of the sky, but in binoculars it is well worth viewing for the beautiful star fields it contains. The four main stars are also an attractive sight in binoculars. About midway between Delta and Gamma, small telescopes will show a bright, dense grouping of stars, M71, which is almost certainly a globular rather than an open cluster.

Sagittarius, the Archer *See page 88.*

Scutum, the Shield *See page 57.*

Serpens Cauda, the Serpent's Tail *See page 57.*

Vulpecula, the Fox

Located south of Cygnus, this constellation is ill-defined and devoid of really bright stars. Binoculars and small telescopes, however, show some attractive star fields in this filamentary region of the Milky Way, as well as a number of other interesting objects.

Perhaps the finest is the Dumbbell Nebula, M27, one of the brightest planetary nebulae in the heavens. It is located due north of Gamma Sagittae in the neighbouring constellation and is best found by reference to that star. Through binoculars, M27 appears as a misty patch, but most telescopes will reveal its characteristic dumbbell shape.

Close to the border with Sagitta, and west of the arrow's "flight", is 4, which lies in a curve of faint stars that form part of a loose open cluster. In binoculars, this curve and a straight line of six stars nearby have the appearance of a coat hanger, and the cluster is often referred to as the "Coathanger".

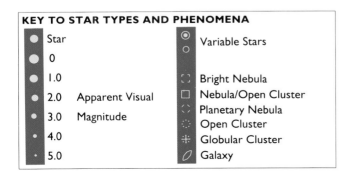

KEY TO STAR TYPES AND PHENOMENA

	Star		Variable Stars
	0		
	1.0		Bright Nebula
	2.0	Apparent Visual	Nebula/Open Cluster
	3.0	Magnitude	Planetary Nebula
	4.0		Open Cluster
	5.0		Globular Cluster
			Galaxy

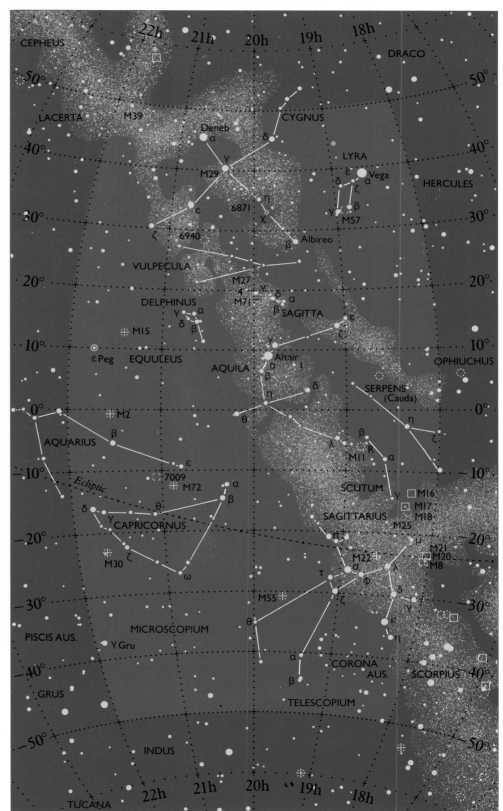

September Stars

As September progresses Pegasus, the Winged Horse, continues chasing the stars of the Summer Triangle towards the western horizon. This signals the approach of autumn in the Northern Hemisphere, and of spring in the Southern.

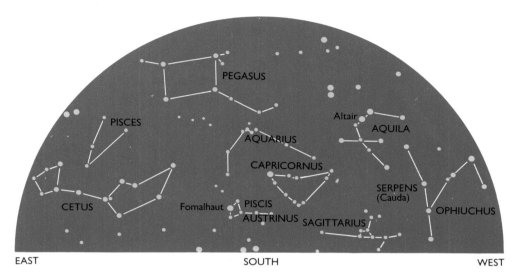

EAST   **SOUTH**   **WEST**

▲ **Northern Hemisphere View of the night sky in mid-latitudes looking south at about 11 pm local time on about September 7.**
This sky view reveals Altair fairly high in the west and Fomalhaut low in the south. Much of the sky is occupied by rather barren constellations.

▼ **Southern Hemisphere View of the night sky in Australia and southern Africa looking north at about 11 pm local time on about September 7.**
Vega and Deneb are now close to the horizon. Pegasus is the most prominent of the rising constellations.

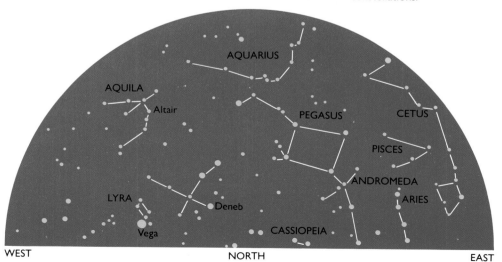

WEST   **NORTH**   **EAST**

Aquarius, the Water-Bearer

This is a sprawling zodiacal constellation, but a faint one, with leading stars of only about the third magnitude. It adjoins other "watery" constellations, Pisces, Cetus, Piscis Austrinus and Capricornus (Fishes, Whale, Southern Fish and Sea Goat).

The brightest star, Alpha, can perhaps best be found by extending a diagonal of the Square of Pegasus from Alpha Andromedae through Alpha Pegasi. Once Alpha is found, the adjacent stars Gamma, Zeta and Eta are easy to spot. The pattern of these four stars represents the mouth of the water jar.

Beta is found just off the extended diagonal through Pegasus. Due north of Beta, and forming a right-angled triangle with Alpha and Beta, is M2. This globular cluster is one of the brightest in the heavens, visible as a misty patch in binoculars and resolved into stars in larger telescopes.

Also worth searching for in Aquarius are two fine planetary nebulae. The brighter of the two is NGC7009, which lies south of a line through Beta and Epsilon, forming a right-angled triangle with them. Seen through larger telescopes, NGC7009 appears to have a ring around it rather like the planet Saturn, and it is called the Saturn Nebula. In the same binocular field of view as the Saturn Nebula is M72, another fairly bright globular cluster.

The other planetary nebula, NGC7293, is called the Helix Nebula because of its spiral appearance in long-exposure photographs. In small telescopes, it looks like a faint smoke ring.

Capricornus, the Sea Goat *See page 58.*

Cygnus, the Swan *See page 84.*

Delphinus, the Dolphin *See page 58.*

Grus, the Crane

This is one of the "southern birds", with outstretched wings and a long neck. The long, slightly curving line of stars that marks the neck and body line are readily spotted looking south from the bright Fomalhaut, in the neighbouring Piscis Austrinus.

The leading star Alpha has a magnitude of 1.7, slightly brighter than the second-magnitude Beta. These two stars provide a nice colour contrast, Alpha being bluish white, Beta being distinctly orange.

Lambda and Iota also have an orange tinge. Delta and Mu are naked-eye doubles, but their pairs of stars are, in reality, far apart.

The area between Theta and the border with the neighbouring constellation Phoenix is well worth exploring in telescopes because it contains a veritable cluster of galaxies.

Lacerta, the Lizard

This northern constellation is small and faint, with only its leading star Alpha above the fourth magnitude. Its zig-zag of stars, however, overlaps a section of the Milky Way between Cassiopeia and Cygnus, and so it contains glittering starscapes that make fine sweeping with binoculars.

One or two fairly bright open clusters are visible in small telescopes, including NGC7243. This one forms an equilateral triangle with Alpha and Beta.

Of great astronomical interest in the constellation, but far too faint to be seen in ordinary amateur instruments, is the object BL Lacertae. It is a variable galaxy, which changes noticeably in brightness in a relatively short time. Astronomers now think it is a quasar.

Pegasus, the Flying Horse *See page 62.*

Phoenix, the Phoenix *See page 62.*

Pisces, the Fishes *See page 63.*

Piscis Austrinus, the Southern Fish

This small constellation is dominated by a single bright star, the first-magnitude Fomalhaut (Fish's Mouth). No other stars are above the fourth magnitude. Although pure white Fomalhaut rates as only the eighteenth brightest star in the heavens, it is easy to spot because it occurs in a region devoid of any other really bright stars.

Perhaps the most interesting star in this otherwise undistinguished constellation is one called Lacaille 9352. Of the eighth magnitude, it is found south of Pi. At a distance of some 11.7 light years, it lies relatively close to Earth and shows a substantial proper motion. It moves noticeably across the background of the other stars over a relatively short period.

Vulpecula, the Fox *See page 59.*

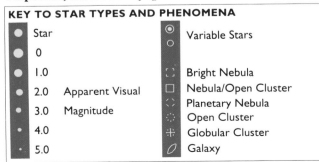

KEY TO STAR TYPES AND PHENOMENA

	Star		Variable Stars
	0		
	1.0		Bright Nebula
	2.0 Apparent Visual		Nebula/Open Cluster
	3.0 Magnitude		Planetary Nebula
	4.0		Open Cluster
	5.0		Globular Cluster
			Galaxy

OCTOBER STARS

The October skies are dominated by the unmistakable Pegasus. With few bright stars, the other constellations are harder to trace. This month is good for observing our galactic neighbour, the Great Spiral in Andromeda.

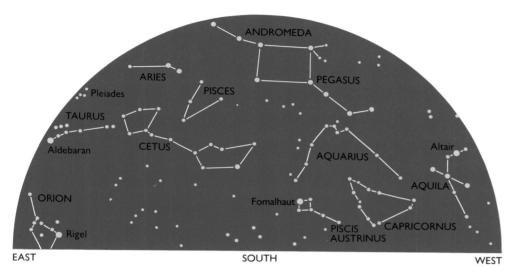

EAST   SOUTH   WEST

▲ **Northern Hemisphere View of the night sky in mid-latitudes looking south at about 11 pm local time on about October 7.** The Square of Pegasus occupies centre stage, while Orion is just rising in the east. Aldebaran and Altair are at a similar altitude.

▼ **Southern Hemisphere View of the night sky in Australia and southern Africa looking north at about 11 pm local time on about October 7.** Pegasus sits in the mid-sky and Orion is appearing over the eastern horizon. Fomalhaut is prominent near the zenith.

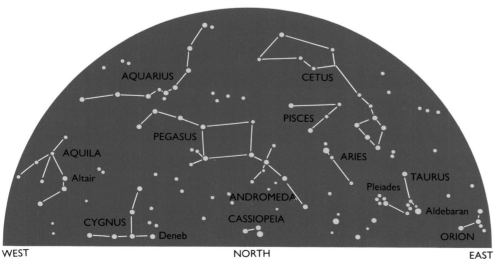

WEST   NORTH   EAST

Andromeda *See page 78.*

Aquarius, the Water-Bearer *See page 60.*

Aries, the Ram *See page 64.*

Cassiopeia *See page 80.*

Cetus, the Whale *See page 64.*

Eridanus *See page 66.*

Grus, the Crane *See page 60.*

Lacerta, the Lizard *See page 61.*

Pegasus, the Flying Horse

This is a large and distinctive constellation, which dominates autumn skies in the Northern Hemisphere. Its four leading stars form one of the most recognizable patterns in the heavens – the Great Square of Pegasus.

Once located, the Square serves as a useful signpost to other constellations. To the naked eye, the area enclosed by the Square is remarkably empty of stars. You would be hard-pressed to see more than a dozen.

Pegasus shares one of the stars in the Square with the neighbouring constellation Andromeda – Alpha Andromedae. (Its Arab name is Alpheratz.) Going clockwise around the Square, the three other stars are Beta (Scheat), Alpha (Markab) and Gamma (Algenib).

All of these stars are of the second magnitude, with Alpha Andromedae being the brightest. Beta is a variable star, although its variation in brightness is not easy to follow. It is a red giant star, and its reddish tinge, apparent even to the naked eye, contrasts with the pure white of Alpha.

The noticeably yellow Epsilon (Enif) lies some distance from the Square, roughly in line with Gamma and Alpha. It is fractionally brighter than Alpha and is a double, whose fainter component can be spotted in binoculars.

Among deep-sky objects in Pegasus, the globular cluster M15 is outstanding. It lies in line with Theta and Epsilon, a fraction too faint to be seen with the naked eye, but readily visible in binoculars and small telescopes. Larger instruments will resolve the outer regions into individual stars. (See the map on page 65 for location.)

Phoenix, the Phoenix

The second-magnitude Alpha marks the eye of this "southern bird", which in mythology was reincarnated from its own ashes. It is a fairly large but rather barren constellation. Beta is a double; both components are yellow and equally bright. Zeta is another double; the brightness of the brighter component varies slightly, and instruments show that it is a close eclipsing binary.

Pisces, the Fishes

This is a large but rather uninteresting constellation of the zodiac, formed of a string of faint stars little brighter than about the fourth magnitude.

One of the two fishes the constellation depicts is marked by a circle of stars south of the Great Square of Pegasus. This is the easiest part of the constellation to identify. The curved line of stars from there to the leading star Alpha is not so easy to follow; nor is the line from Alpha to Eta and beyond.

Alpha is a close double star, separated in larger telescopes into bluish white components. Zeta is a much wider double, with twin pale yellow stars.

Among several galaxies in Pisces, M74 is the brightest. Located close to Eta, it can just be picked up by small telescopes.

Piscis Austrinus, the Southern Fish *See page 61.*

Sculptor, the Sculptor

With Phoenix and Fornax, this constellation appears in a relatively barren region of the mid-southern skies. It is best found by reference to the bright Fomalhaut in the neighbouring Piscis Austrinus.

Sculptor is notable mainly for its galaxies, several of which (if you can find them!) can be glimpsed in binoculars. Larger telescopes will pick up many more. Definitely in binocular range is NGC253, visible as an elongated misty patch about a third of the way along a line from Alpha towards Beta Ceti to the north. Larger telescopes reveal NGC253 to be a spiral galaxy, much like our own but smaller.

NGC253 is the brightest member of a cluster of galaxies in the region, known as the Sculptor group. They lie about 10 million light years away.

Triangulum, the Triangle *See page 65.*

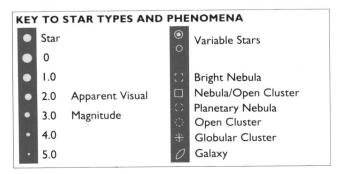

KEY TO STAR TYPES AND PHENOMENA

●	Star	◉	Variable Stars	
●	0	○		
●	1.0			
●	2.0	Apparent Visual	⬚	Bright Nebula
●	3.0	Magnitude	☐	Nebula/Open Cluster
·	4.0		⌣	Planetary Nebula
·	5.0		⬭	Open Cluster
			✳	Globular Cluster
			∅	Galaxy

November Stars

As Pegasus begins its slow descent in the west, Taurus and Orion begin climbing to prominence in the east. Orange Aldebaran, the Hyades and the Pleiades clusters are becoming well placed for observation in both hemispheres.

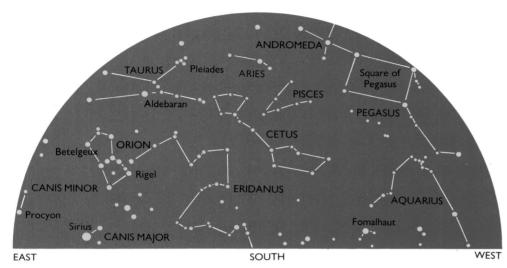

EAST   **SOUTH**   **WEST**

▲ **Northern Hemisphere View of the night sky in mid-latitudes looking south at about 11 pm local time on about November 7.**
Faint constellations such as Eridanus and Cetus cover much of the sky. The interest lies in the east, in sparkling Orion and Taurus.

▼ **Southern Hemisphere View of the night sky in Australia and southern Africa looking north at about 11 pm local time on about November 7.**
Pegasus and Andromeda are about to set in the west. In the east, Aldebaran, Betelgeux and Rigel form a nice triangle.

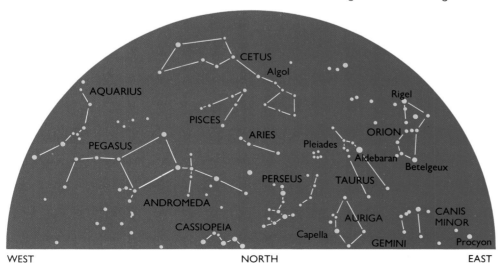

WEST   **NORTH**   **EAST**

Andromeda *See page 78.*

Aries, the Ram
This small constellation of the zodiac has just two noticeably bright stars, the second-magnitude Alpha and the somewhat less bright Beta. This pair can probably best be found by reference to the Great Square of Pegasus. Alpha is also at the same declination as the Pleiades cluster in the neighbouring Taurus.

Gamma, due south of Beta, is a fine double, visible in small telescopes as a pair of equally bright bluish white stars.

Cetus, the Whale
Although it is one of the largest constellations in the heavens, Cetus is not easy to trace because of its lack of bright stars. Only Alpha in the Whale's head and Beta in its tail are above the third magnitude.

However, both these and the other main stars lie more or less on a line between Antares in Taurus and Fomalhaut in Piscis Austrinus.

In the Whale's head, Alpha is a wide binocular double. It is a red giant, whose orange tinge is discernible to the naked eye and very obvious through binoculars. A telescope is needed to split the adjacent bright double star, Gamma, into its two components, which provide a marked colour contrast of bluish white and yellow.

In the tail region of Cetus, Tau is interesting in that it is a star of a similar type to the Sun. Some 12 light years away, it is one of the closest stars that astronomers think could have a planetary system like the Sun's. It is a favourite target for SETI (searches for extraterrestrial intelligence) projects.

Historically, the most important star in the constellation is Omicron, also called Mira, meaning "wonderful". It is the prototype long-period variable star, a huge red giant that varies widely in brightness over a period of several months or a year or more.

Mira Ceti varies between magnitudes of about 3 and 10 every 11 months or so. It is found midway between Gamma and the distinctive pair Zeta and Chi, and is easily seen when it is near maximum, but difficult to find when it is near minimum.

A number of galaxies lie near Delta, the brightest of which, M77, can be sighted in binoculars as a hazy patch. A telescope will show it is a face-on spiral with bright, widely spaced arms. It is one of the most remote Messier objects, lying at a distance of over 50 million light years.

Eridanus *See page 66.*

Fornax, the Furnace *See page 66.*

Pegasus, the Flying Horse *See page 62.*

Perseus *See page 67.*

Phoenix, the Phoenix *See page 62.*

Pisces, the Fishes *See page 63.*

Sculptor, the Sculptor *See page 63.*

Triangulum, the Triangle

With its three main stars arranged in a neat triangle, this constellation is well named. However, it is far from bright, with just two stars, Alpha and Beta, of about the third magnitude. The third main star, Gamma, makes up the third corner of the triangle, along with two close fainter companions.

Triangulum's main claim to fame is the beautiful face-on spiral galaxy M33, which lies about midway between Alpha Trianguli, and Beta Andromedae in the neighbouring constellation. It is just about visible to the naked eye on a really dark night, and can readily be seen as a hazy patch in binoculars. Larger telescopes, however, are needed to bring out its wide-open spiral arms.

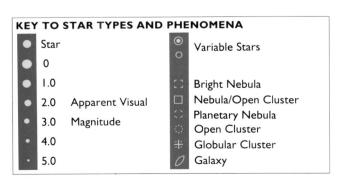

KEY TO STAR TYPES AND PHENOMENA

	Star		Variable Stars
	0		
	1.0		
	2.0	Apparent Visual	Bright Nebula
	3.0	Magnitude	Nebula/Open Cluster
			Planetary Nebula
	4.0		Open Cluster
	5.0		Globular Cluster
			Galaxy

December Stars

A hexagonal arrangement of bright stars – Sirius, Rigel, Aldebaran, Capella, Pollux and Procyon – in Canis Major, Orion, Auriga, Gemini and Canis Minor make for spectacular star-gazing in this month and the next.

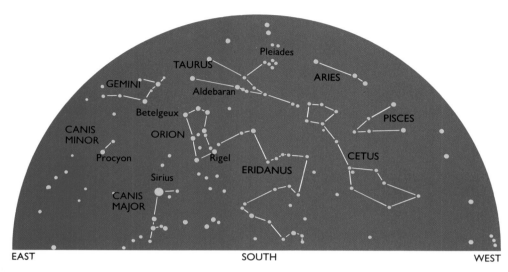

EAST   SOUTH   WEST

▲ **Northern Hemisphere View of the night sky in mid-latitudes looking south at about 11 pm local time on about December 7.**
The meridian neatly splits the sky into two. The eastern half sparkles with bright stars and provides a marked contrast to the lacklustre western half.

▼ **Southern Hemisphere View of the night sky in Australia and southern Africa looking north at about 11 pm local time on about December 7.**
The December hexagon of bright stars is stunning in the east. The Pleiades cluster is in an ideal viewing position.

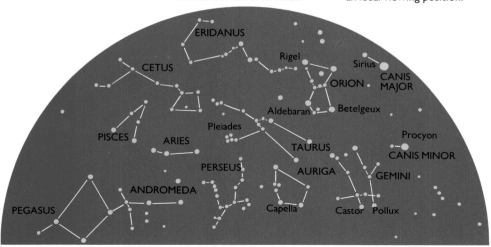

WEST   NORTH   EAST

Aries, the Ram *See page 64.*

Auriga, the Charioteer *See page 44.*

Carina, the Keel *See page 42.*

Cetus, the Whale *See page 64.*

Columba, the Dove *See page 45.*

Eridanus
One of the largest of the constellations, Eridanus represents a river. The ancient Middle Eastern astronomers associated it with their life-giving rivers Euphrates and the Nile.

With broad meanders, Eridanus winds itself through the heavens. It "rises" at Beta, near the bright Rigel in Orion, and works its way lazily towards the brilliant Alpha far south. The Arab name for Alpha, Achernar, means "end of the river". Achernar, of magnitude 0.5, is the ninth brightest star in the sky.

Heading "upstream" from Achernar, Theta is perhaps the first interesting star. It is a fine double, which small telescopes will separate as a bluish white pair.

The other interesting stars lie in the northern reaches of the river. Omicron^2 is a wide and easy double. The fainter of its components is a white dwarf star, and is the easiest of its type to see. Larger telescopes reveal that the white dwarf itself has a companion, a red dwarf.

Delta and Pi are both distinctly orange and form an obvious triangle with Epsilon. Epsilon lies relatively close to Earth (10.7 light years) and is a similar type of star to the Sun. Astronomers have long thought that it might have a planetary system like Earth's.

Fornax, the Furnace
This is one of the faint constellations in mid-southern skies, which, like the neighbouring Sculptor, lacks prominent stars. Only Alpha is brighter, just, than the fourth magnitude. Mostly, Fornax is encircled by one of the broad meanders of Eridanus.

Although binoculars find little of interest, small telescopes begin to reveal the riches Fornax possesses. Zeroing in on the faint twin stars Lambda reveals a dense star cluster nearby. Larger instruments show it to be an irregular galaxy, called the Fornax System. It is a dwarf galaxy, like the Magellanic Clouds.

On the edge of the constellation, close to the triangle of stars, g, f and h Eridani, telescopes reveal the Fornax Cluster of galaxies. Larger instruments show the Cluster to have about 18 members, one of which is NGC1365, one of the brightest barred-spiral galaxies in the heavens.

At a distance of about 55 million light years, the Fornax Cluster is one of the nearest clusters of galaxies.

Lepus, the Hare *See page 45.*

Orion *See page 86.*

Perseus

This bright northern constellation has some splendid stars and glorious star fields, since it straddles the Milky Way. The brightest star, Alpha (also called by its Arab name Mirfak), is surrounded by a myriad of faint stars, and the group prettily fills the whole field in binoculars.

Binoculars will also reveal the rare beauty of one of the showpiece features of Perseus, the famous Double Cluster. Also called the Sword Handle, it is easily located midway between Gamma Persei and Delta Cassiopeiae in the neighbouring constellation. It is a pair of glorious open clusters, each of which would be beautiful by itself. The keen-eyed should see them without optical aid on a dark night. On star charts they are usually separately identified as h and Chi Persei, or NGC 869 and 884.

The other showpiece feature in Perseus is Beta. Its Arab name Algol, or the Winking Demon, describes it well. For most of the time, it shines steadily at about magnitude 2, but about every 2½ days it fades over a few hours to about magnitude 3.5 before regaining its former brightness. Algol is a classic example of an eclipsing binary and was the first of its type to be recognized.

In the same binocular field as Algol is another open cluster, M34, which is just visible to the naked eye.

Taurus, the Bull *See page 92.*

Triangulum, the Triangle *See page 65.*

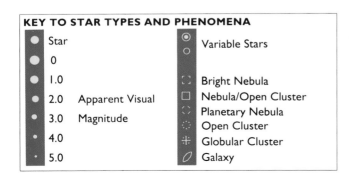

KEY TO STAR TYPES AND PHENOMENA

● Star		◉	Variable Stars
● 0		○	
● 1.0			
● 2.0	Apparent Visual	⬚	Bright Nebula
		◻	Nebula/Open Cluster
● 3.0	Magnitude	⟨⟩	Planetary Nebula
		⬭	Open Cluster
● 4.0		✢	Globular Cluster
· 5.0		⬭	Galaxy

▲ The brilliant star Capella in Auriga, which is the third brightest star in northern skies, after Arcturus in Boötes and Vega in Lyra, and the sixth brightest star in the whole heavens.

STAR ANATOMY

Stars are great globes of searing hot gas, which generate enormous energy in their interior and radiate it into space. All the stars except one lie very far away from us, at distances measured in million-millions of kilometres. The nearby star is the one we call the Sun.

The Sun is very special to us, but in the Universe as a whole it is very ordinary. It is not particularly big, nor particularly bright. There are many millions of other stars in the night sky like it. But we know of millions of other stars that are quite unlike it: red giant and supergiant stars of truly gigantic dimensions; stars tinier than planets; stars many thousands of times brighter than the Sun; and stars that fluctuate wildly in brightness.

Magnitudes of brightness

As a quick glance at the night sky shows, the stars vary widely in brightness. Stars like Sirius, Canopus, Alpha Centauri and Arcturus shine like celestial beacons, while others are scarcely visible to the naked eye.

In about 150 BC, the Greek astronomer Hipparchus devised a scale of "magnitudes" for grading the brightness of stars. He allotted a magnitude of 1 to the brightest stars, and a magnitude of 6 to those just visible to the naked eye.

This system forms the basis of the magnitude scale astronomers still use today. But they have refined and extended it. On the scale, a star of the first magnitude (magnitude 1) is 100 times brighter than a star of the sixth magnitude. This means that a star of the first magnitude is about two-and-a-half times brighter than one of the second magnitude, which is two-and-a-half times brighter than one of the third magnitude, and so on.

Because brightness can now be accurately measured with instruments such as photometers, magnitudes can be expressed accurately to one or two decimal places. Deneb, for example, has a magnitude of 1.25. (In this book, however, magnitudes are usually expressed to the first decimal place for simplicity.)

To express the brightness of stars beyond naked-eye range, the magnitude scale is extended forwards beyond magnitude 6. The closest star to us after the Sun, Proxima Centauri, has a magnitude of 11.1. The most powerful telescopes are able to detect stars as faint as magnitude 25.

To measure the brightness of exceptionally bright stars such as Sirius, the scale is extended backwards from

BRIGHTEST STARS

Brightest Stars	Designation	App. magnitude	Absolute magnitude	Spectral type	Distance (Light years)
Sun	—	−26.7	4.8	G2	—
Sirius	α Canis Majoris	−1.5	1.4	A1	8.8
Canopus	α Carinae	−0.7	−4.7	F0	196
Rigil Kent	α Centauri	−0.3	4.4	G2	4.3
Arcturus	α Boötis	−0.1	−0.2	K1	37
Vega	α Lyrae	0.0	0.5	A0	26
Capella	α Aurigae	0.1	−0.6	G8	46
Rigel	β Orionis	0.1	−7.0	B8	815
Procyon	α Canis Minoris	0.4	2.7	F5	11
Achernar	α Eridani	0.5	−2.2	B5	127
Hadar	β Centauri	0.6	−5.0	B1	391
Altair	α Aquilae	0.8	2.3	A7	16
Betelgeux	α Orionis	0.8	−6.0	M2	652
Aldebaran	α Tauri	0.8	−0.7	K5	68
Acrux	α Crucis	0.9	−3.5	B1	261
Spica	α Virginis	1.0	−3.4	B1	261
Antares	α Scorpii	1.0	−4.7	M1	424
Pollux	β Geminorum	1.1	1.0	K0	36
Fomalhaut	α Piscis Austrini	1.2	1.9	A3	23
Deneb	α Cygni	1.3	−7.3	A2	1630
Mimosa	β Crucis	1.3	−4.7	B0	490
Regulus	α Leonis	1.4	−0.6	B7	85

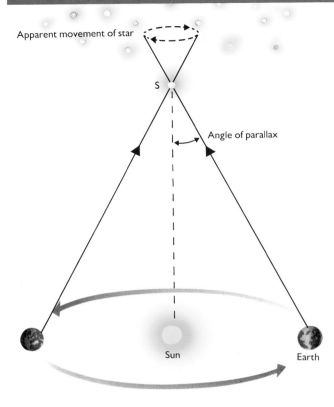

Apparent movement of star

S

Angle of parallax

Sun

Earth

▲ We can measure the distance to a few nearby stars using the principle of parallax. We note the different positions of the star S against the background of distant stars when viewed from opposite ends of the Earth's orbit. We can work out the star's distance using trigonometry.

magnitude 1 into negative values. So Sirius has a magnitude of –1.46. On this same scale, the brightest planet, Venus, can reach a magnitude of –4.4; the Moon is –12.7, and the Sun –26.7.

The brightness of a star that we observe from Earth is only an apparent brightness. It bears little relation to the star's true brightness: a nearby truly dim star will appear brighter than a very distant truly bright star.

To compare the true brightness of stars, we would have to view them from the same distance. And that is the basis of the scale of true or absolute magnitude astronomers use. They define the absolute magnitude of a star as the magnitude they would observe if the star were at a distance of 10 parsecs (see below). On this absolute scale, Sirius now rates only 1.4, whereas Antares rates –4.7. Some stars, such as Rigel, rate more than –7.

Distance to the stars

No matter how powerful a telescope you have, you can never see the stars other than as pinpoints of light. That is because they are so far away that their light takes years to reach us. Indeed, we often express the distance to a star in terms of the number of years it takes for its light to reach us. The light from Sirius takes 8.8 years to reach us, so we can say that Sirius is 8.8 "light years" away, 1 light year being the distance light travels in a year (9.5 million million kilometres, 5.9 million million miles).

In this book we express stellar distances in terms of light years. But professional astronomers generally use a unit called the parsec, which is equivalent to about 3.3

Star

Actual path of star

Radial motion

Proper motion

Earth

▲ All the stars are moving relative to us. For just a few, we can detect their proper motion, or motion across our line of sight.

NEAREST STARS

Nearest Stars	Distance (Light years)	Proper motion ("/yr)	App. magnitude	Absolute magnitude	Spectral type
Proxima Centauri	4.3	3.9	11.1	15.5	M5
α Centauri A	4.3	3.7	–0.3	4.4	G2
α Centauri B	4.3	3.7	1.3	5.7	K5
Barnard's Star	5.9	10.3	9.5	13.3	M5
Wolf 359	7.6	4.7	13.5	16.7	M8
Lalande 21185	8.1	4.8	7.5	10.5	M2
Sirius A	8.8	1.3	–1.5	1.4	A1
Sirius B	8.8	1.3	8.7	11.6	A
Luyten 726–8A	8.9	3.4	12.5	15.3	M5
UV Ceti	8.9	3.4	13.0	15.8	M6
Ross 154	9.4	0.7	10.6	13.3	M4
Ross 248	10.3	1.6	12.3	14.8	M6
ε Eridani	10.8	1.0	3.7	6.1	K2
Luyten 789–6	10.8	3.3	12.2	14.6	M7
Ross 128	10.8	1.4	11.1	13.5	M5
61 Cygni A	11.1	5.2	5.2	7.6	K5
61 Cygni B	11.1	5.2	6.0	8.4	K7
ε Indi	11.2	4.7	4.7	7.0	K5
Procyon A	11.4	1.3	0.4	2.7	F5
Procyon B	11.4	1.3	10.7	13.0	F
Struve 2398 A	11.5	2.3	8.9	11.2	M4
Struve 2398 B	11.5	2.3	9.7	12.0	M5

▼ The size of stars varies enormously. Our star the Sun is classed as a yellow dwarf. It is small compared with hotter blue-white stars like Spica. But, some 5,000 million years hence, it will swell up into a giant. Bigger stars expand into supergiants, with diameters measured in many hundreds of millions of kilometres.

Yellow dwarf

Blue-white star

Red giant

Supergiant

Larger giant

▲ A star's spectrum provides a means of classifying it. The top spectrum is typical of white stars like Deneb, with a surface temperature of about 11,000°C (20,000°F). The bottom spectrum is typical of red stars like Betelgeux, with a surface temperature of only about 3,000°C (5,000°F).

light years. (1 parsec is the distance at which a star would show an angle of parallax of one second of arc, or 1/3600 of a degree; see diagram, left.)

The message in starlight

Although the stars lie very far away, we know a lot about them. We can often tell how hot they are, what they are made of, how fast they are moving, and so on. All this information – and more – we can extract from the feeble light that reaches us through space. We get at it by passing the light through the most important astronomical instrument after the telescope – the spectroscope (or spectrograph). This instrument splits up starlight into a spectrum, a spread of different light wavelengths, or colours, from violet-blue (shortest waves) to red. A series of dark lines crosses the spectrum at intervals.

Stars have different kinds of spectra. For example, some are brightest in blue, some in yellow, some in red, and so on. Their colour intensity is a measure of their surface temperature. Spectra also differ in the number and arrangement of dark lines. From the position of the lines we can tell, for example, the star's composition. We can also tell how fast and in which direction the star is moving. If the star is travelling towards us, the spectral lines are shifted bodily towards the blue end of the spectrum. If it is travelling away from us, the spectral lines are shifted towards the red end. The amount of shift is a measure of the star's speed.

The spectrum provides a useful way of classifying a star, because stars of a similar type have a similar kind of

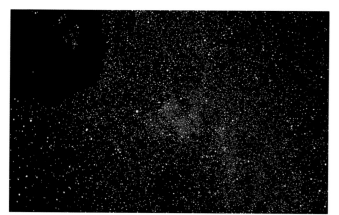

◄ The Hertzsprung-Russell diagram relates the absolute brightness and the spectral class of stars. Most stars lie on a diagonal, called the Main Sequence.

▲ This dense star field is in Cygnus. The brightest star in the picture is Deneb. This star has an absolute magnitude of at least −7.3 and is one of the most luminous stars known.

Brightness   Primary eclipse   Secondary eclipse

Eclipsing binaries

The star Beta Persei is named Algol, or "The Winking Demon", because every 69 hours it suddenly dims from its regular magnitude of about 2 to about magnitude 4. The first person to explain Algol's odd behaviour was the deaf-and-dumb English astronomer John Goodricke in 1783.

Algol behaves as it does because it belongs to a class of stars called eclipsing binaries. It consists of two stars orbiting around each other: one large and dim, and the other small and bright. The plane of their orbit is in our line of sight, so periodically they pass in front of, or eclipse, each other. When the dim one eclipses the bright one, the brightness suddenly drops markedly. But there is only a slight drop in brightness when the dim one is eclipsed.

spectrum. There are ten main kinds of spectra, or spectral classes, designated O, B, A, F, G, K, M, R, N and S, in order of decreasing surface temperatures, which run from about 40,000° to below 3,000°C (72,000°–5,000°F). (This sequence of spectral classes can be remembered by the never-to-be-forgotten mnemonic "Oh Be A Fine Girl Kiss Me Right Now Sweetie"!)

The spectral class and absolute magnitude (see page 69) are two of the basic characteristics of a star. When they are plotted against one another, the stars fall into distinct groups. The resulting plot is called the Hertzsprung-Russell (H-R) Diagram, after the astronomers who first devised it, Ejnar Hertzsprung in Denmark and Henry Russell in the United States.

A version of the H-R Diagram for some of the best-known stars appears on the opposite page. Most stars, including our own Sun, lie on the diagonal band called the Main Sequence. Stars spend most of their life, shining steadily, on the Main Sequence.

The variable stars

Most of the stars we see in the sky shine steadily. (They "twinkle", it is true, but this is because of air currents in the Earth's atmosphere.) However, some stars vary noticeably in brightness over a short or long period, and are called variable stars.

The star Beta Persei, or Algol, varies in brightness every 69 hours. But that is because it is a two-star, or binary, system in which one star periodically eclipses another. We know of many "eclipsing binaries" like it.

Other stars vary in brightness because of processes going on inside them. The first to be discovered was Omicron Ceti, or Mira (meaning "Wonderful"), which varies between magnitudes 3 and 10 in about 330 days. Mira typifies what are known as long-period variables, which are believed to be pulsating red giant stars.

Other variable stars vary over much shorter periods, for example, Delta Cephei, which is the prototype star for the Cepheid variables (see below).

Novae

Sometimes a bright new star suddenly appears in the sky, and we call it a nova (meaning "new"). In fact, it is not a new star at all, but an existing dim star that has suddenly increased dramatically in brightness, typically by many thousands of times. This can happen over only a few hours. The subsequent decline in brightness to normality is more gradual.

But the most dramatic "new star" occurrences are supernovae. They happen when supergiant stars blast themselves apart in their death throes (see page 72).

The Cepheids

The variable star Delta Cephei fluctuates in brightness with extreme regularity, varying between magnitudes 3.5 and 4.3 in precisely 5.366 days, as this light curve shows.

Many other stars vary regularly in the same way, and they are known as the Cepheids. The typical, or classical Cepheids have periods ranging from one to about 50 days. Polaris is a Cepheid with a period of nearly four days.

In 1912 Henrietta Leavitt in the USA discovered that the period of a Cepheid is directly related to its absolute magnitude, or luminosity. This law enables us to measure the distance to a Cepheid wherever it may be.

Star Life and Death

The lifetime of a star is measured in hundreds or thousands of millions of years, so we cannot trace the life-cycle of any particular star from beginning to end. However, we can study stars of different ages and so piece together the life-cycle of a typical star.

▲ A newborn star (arrowed) in the nebula Barnard 5 in Perseus, spotted by the infrared astronomy satellite IRAS. At present, the temperature and pressure in this protostar's interior are not yet high enough to trigger off nuclear reactions.

Stars are born in nebulae – the billowing clouds of dust and gas (mainly hydrogen) that exist between the stars in the galaxies. Star formation begins when a particularly dense part of a nebula begins to condense, or starts to shrink, under the influence of gravity.

No one knows for certain what triggers the process. It could be the shock waves that ripple through space after another star explodes and dies. That would be neat: the death of one star triggering the birth of another.

As the nebula shrinks under gravity, it releases energy, which appears as heat. The smaller the collapsing nebula (or "protostar") becomes, the hotter it gets. Event-

◀ The Dumbbell Nebula (M27) in Vulpecula. The distinctive shape of this planetary nebula is caused by a shell of expanding gas and dust, puffed out by the central star millions of years ago.

ually, temperatures inside reach over 10,000,000°C (18,000,000°F). Then the nuclei (centres) of the hydrogen atoms begin to fuse, or join together. This nuclear fusion process produces fantastic amounts of energy as light, heat and other kinds of radiation. The radiation eventually makes its way to the surface, and escapes into space and the body starts to shine, as a star. What happens to the star from then on depends on its mass.

A star like the Sun shines steadily for about 10,000 million years. Then with its hydrogen fuel exhausted, it swells up into a red giant star with a diameter tens of times bigger than before. In time, the red giant begins to shrink, occasionally puffing off gas which astronomers detect as a planetary nebula. As the dying star shrinks, it heats up, becoming a small, hot white dwarf.

Stars more massive than the Sun meet a more spectacular end. They expand beyond the red-giant stage into a supergiant, with hundreds of times their original diameter. A supergiant is unstable and soon collapses. This triggers off a cataclysmic explosion – a supernova – in which most of the star is blasted into space.

The outcome of a supernova explosion again depends on the original mass of the star. Stars with a mass up to about seven times that of the Sun leave behind a very dense neutron star, typically only about 20–30 kilometres (12–20 miles) across. Stars with even greater mass are virtually crushed out of existence. They leave behind a region of space with such enormous gravity that nothing, not even light, can escape from it. We call such a region a black hole.

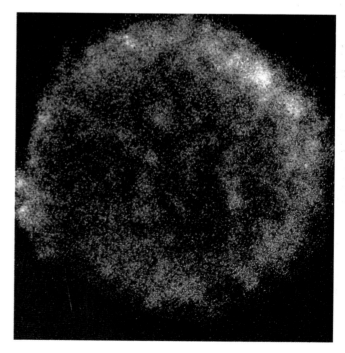

► The remnants of a supernova witnessed by the celebrated Danish astronomer Tycho Brahe in 1572. It is an X-ray image, taken by the German Rosat (Roentgen satellite). Tycho is one of the few supernova remnants whose age we know precisely from recorded observations.

Supernova 1987A

In the early morning of February 20, 1987, astronomer Ian Shelton became the first person for centuries to witness a supernova with the naked eye. He was observing at the Las Campanas Observatory in Chile, South America.

The supernova, SN 1987A, took place in our galactic neighbour, the Large Magellanic Cloud. It occurred when the supergiant star Sanduleak −69° 202 exploded. It has been the most widely studied of any supernova.

▲ SN 1987A at maximum brightness, outshining every star in the Large Magellanic Cloud. It occurred close to what is ordinarily the highlight of the galaxy, the Tarantula Nebula.

▶ The expanding ring of material blasted into space during the SN 1987A explosion is shown in the middle of this picture returned by the Hubble Space Telescope. A core of debris at the centre is what remains of the exploding star.

◄ The Trifid Nebula (M20) is one of the many astronomical delights in Sagittarius. A most distinctive nebula, it is named after the dark dust lanes that split it into fan-shaped segments. The Trifid is an unusual combination of an emission nebula (the main red cloud) and a reflection nebula (the fainter blue one).

3

KEY CONSTELLATIONS

Of the 88 constellations that cover the celestial sphere, a number are truly outstanding for one reason or another. In the Southern Hemisphere they include Sagittarius. This constellation is magnificent not so much for its stars but for the abundance of clusters and nebulae (like the Trifid, left) it contains, and for its dense star clouds. In the Northern Hemisphere Taurus boasts two exceptional star clusters. Orion, which spans the celestial equator, displays fine stars, brilliant nebulae, and acts as a signpost for locating stars in other constellations.

Sagittarius, Taurus and Orion are three of the eleven key constellations that we feature in this chapter for more detailed investigation. The others are Andromeda, Cassiopeia, Centaurus and Crux, Cygnus, Scorpius, Ursa Major and Virgo.

Each constellation (except for Centaurus and Crux) rates a double-page spread, with the constellation map occupying a full page. The descriptive text is prefaced by the fascinating story behind the mythological figure the constellation purports to resemble.

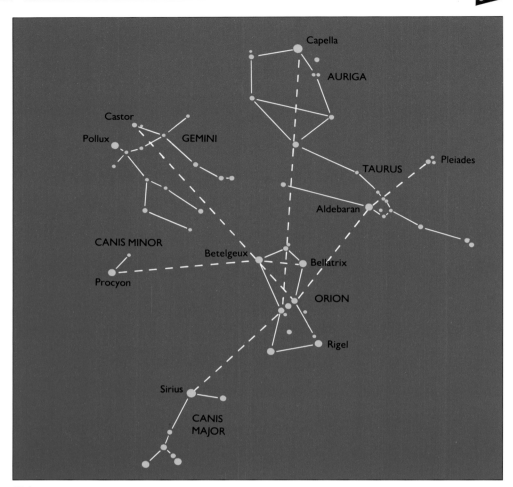

Orion

Orion, too, is an excellent celestial signpost. Spanning the celestial equator, it is a useful constellation for observers in both hemispheres. The line through the three stars of Orion's Belt south to Sirius and north to Aldebaran and the Pleiades is particularly striking.

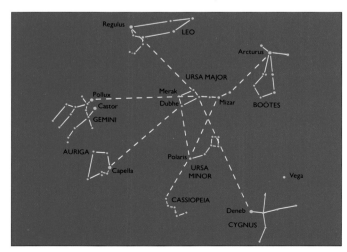

Ursa Major

In the Northern Hemisphere, Ursa Major is indeed a key constellation. The Plough, or Big Dipper, serves as an invaluable signpost for pointing the way to a host of other stars.

SIGNPOSTS IN THE SKY

The eleven constellations featured in this chapter are among the most spectacular in the heavens. They are drawn from both the northern and the southern hemispheres. Each has more than its fair share of coloured stars and variables, doubles and clusters, and nebulae and galaxies. Many of them, moreover, are invaluable in guiding astronomers around the sky.

There is no other celestial signpost in the heavens to rival the Plough, or Big Dipper, the most prominent part of Ursa Major. Although it boasts no star of the first magnitude, the Plough is quite unmistakable, which is a good start! If you look at the diagram on the bottom left, you can see just how useful it can be.

The four stars that form the share, or blade, of the Plough act in pairs as pointers, not only to the Pole Star, Polaris, but also to Deneb in Cygnus, Capella in Auriga, Pollux and twin Castor in Gemini, and Regulus in Leo. Following the curve of the Plough handle brings you to Arcturus, the brightest star in northern skies. And by continuing the curve further, you reach Spica in Virgo.

Orion (*left*) is unmistakable too. Its shape is distinctive and its stars are bright, with two – Betelgeux and Rigel – being of the first magnitude. The three stars in Orion's Belt are pointers to brightest-star-in-the-sky Sirius in Canis Major and Aldebaran in Taurus, the fiery eye of the bull. A diagonal through Rigel and Betelgeux leads to

▼ One of the many highlights of the key constellation Orion is the Great Nebula (M42), in which is embedded the multiple star called the Trapezium. This picture shows clearly the star's four components.

Castor and its twin Pollux. Going almost due east from Gamma Orionis, or Bellatrix, leads you to Procyon in Canis Minor. Capella is found on a line running north through the middle of the main star pattern.

The most obvious pointers in far southern skies are Alpha and Beta Centauri, which guide the eye to the Southern Cross, or Crux. Without them, the eye might be tempted to mistake the so-called False Cross, not far away, for the real one. The False Cross is made up of a pair of stars from Vela and a pair from Carina. Unlike the Northern Hemisphere, the Southern Hemisphere has no convenient pole star, nor even pointers in the right direction. The long axis of the Southern Cross, however, points nearly in the right direction.

Epoch 2000

It must be said that the positions of the stars on the celestial sphere on the maps that follow – and on those in Chapter 2 – are not quite accurate. They are shown in the positions they will occupy on January 1, 2000. The year 2000 is the so-called standard epoch of observation. But the difference between the stars' present positions and those for Epoch 2000 is now negligible.

The reason why the positions of the stars change slowly is precession. This is the "wobbling" of the Earth's axis, which causes the celestial poles to describe a circle in space once about every 26,000 years. Because of precession, Deneb in Cygnus will become the pole star in about AD 10,000.

▼ This star cloud in the key constellation Sagittarius is the brightest in the sky. Easily seen with the naked eye, it is magnificent in binoculars, like all parts of the Milky Way in Sagittarius.

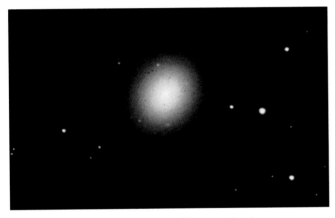

▲ In the key constellation Andromeda is the incomparable Great Spiral galaxy, on the edge of which is this elliptical galaxy, M32. This is one of the two companions of the Great Spiral.

▼ In the Southern Hemisphere Centaurus and Crux are key constellations. This photograph shows (*at right*) Alpha and Beta Centauri pointing to the unmistakable Southern Cross.

ANDROMEDA

Andromeda was the beautiful daughter of King Cepheus and Queen Cassiopeia. By boasting about her own beauty (see page 80), the Queen upset Poseidon, the sea god, who sent a monster, Cetus, to terrorize the shores of Cepheus's kingdom. To placate Poseidon, the King chained Andromeda to rocks on the shore as a sacrifice. Just as Cetus was about to pounce on her, the hero Perseus happened by and killed it. He later wed Andromeda.

This large constellation is easily found because it is linked to one of the most distinctive constellations in the heavens, Pegasus. The leading star, Alpha Andromedae, or Alpheratz, forms the north-east corner of the Square of Pegasus.

Andromeda has its fair share of doubles, variables and clusters, but it is best known for a fuzzy patch of light that looks like a nebula, but isn't, and is clearly visible to the naked eye. M31 in the Messier catalogue, this fuzzy patch used to be called the Great Nebula in Andromeda. However, we now know that it is a neighbouring galaxy similar to our own, but considerably bigger and containing many more stars.

The Great Spiral

The Andromeda Galaxy is one of the showpiece objects of the northern heavens. It is a spiral galaxy like our own, but is much bigger, with a diameter of 150,000 light years. It is in fact the largest galaxy in our Local Group of galaxies, and is well named the Great Spiral.

Of about the fourth magnitude in brightness, the Great Spiral is easily seen near Nu. It lies about 2.3 million light years away, which makes it easily the farthest naked-eye object in the night sky.

In binoculars the Great Spiral shows as a distinct oval, while larger telescopes bring out individual stars and a dark dust lane. M31 also has two companion galaxies, M32 and M110 (NGC205), both visible in binoculars.

Interesting companions

Among Andromeda's more interesting stars is the second-magnitude Gamma. One of the most beautiful doubles in the night sky, it is readily resolved in small telescopes into a bright golden yellow primary and a bluish green companion. The companion is also a double, but resolved only in larger telescopes.

An easier double than Gamma is Pi, while a harder one, with yellow components, is 36 Andromedae, located between Eta and Zeta near the border with Pisces.

Among the variable stars in the constellation is the distinctly red Mira-type R Andromedae. It is located close to a trio of fifth-magnitude stars Theta, Rho and Sigma, north of Alpha in the Square of Pegasus. It comes into binocular range at its brightest (about magnitude 7) but fades to magnitude 14. It is a pulsating red giant star, varying over a period of 409 days.

A green doughnut

Following an arc through Lambda, Kappa and Iota leads you to NGC7662, one of the brighter planetary nebulae. In small telescopes it looks like a fuzzy greenish star, but larger instruments reveal the doughnut-shaped disc and the very hot central star.

South of Gamma is a trio of stars, 59, 58 and 56. Close to 56, which is a wide double, is a fairly scattered open cluster NGC752. Next to Beta (Mirach) is NGC404, an elliptical galaxy which has a fuzzy appearance similar to that of a developing comet.

East of Gamma, in the direction of Algol in the adjoining constellation, is NGC891, which is a classic edge-on spiral, bisected with a dark dust lane. But only larger telescopes will pick this up.

▼ The central part of the Great Spiral, M31. This bright region presents itself as an oval in binoculars. The streak in the picture marks the path of a satellite passing overhead at the time the exposure was being made.

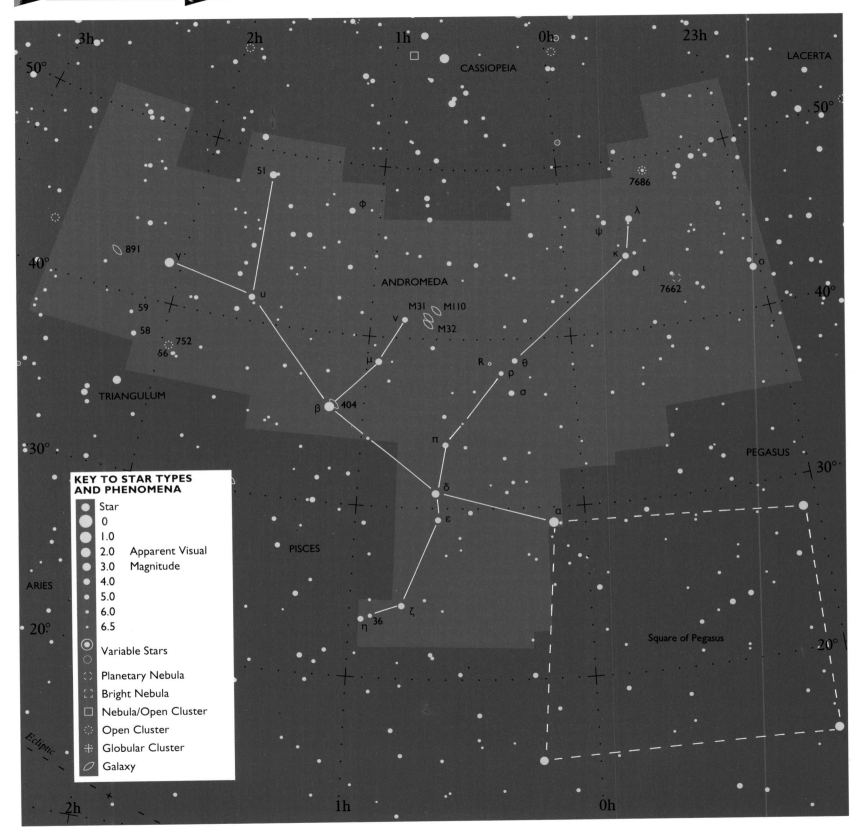

3h 2h 1h 0h 23h

LACERTA

50°

CASSIOPEIA

50°

51

7686

Φ

λ

ψ

40°

891 γ

κ

ι

40°

υ

ANDROMEDA

7662

59

M31 M110

58

ν

M32

752

56

μ

R ρ θ

σ

β 404

TRIANGULUM

30°

π

PEGASUS

30°

δ

**KEY TO STAR TYPES
AND PHENOMENA**

α

Star

0

1.0

2.0   Apparent Visual

PISCES

3.0   Magnitude

4.0

ARIES

5.0

6.0

20°

6.5

ζ

Variable Stars

η 36

Square of Pegasus

20°

Planetary Nebula

Bright Nebula

Nebula/Open Cluster

Open Cluster

Globular Cluster

Ecliptic

Galaxy

2h

1h

0h

CASSIOPEIA

Queen Cassiopeia was the vain wife of King Cepheus and the mother of Andromeda. It was a consequence of the Queen's vanity that Andromeda nearly met an untimely end in the jaws of the sea monster Cetus. Cassiopeia boasted that she was fairer than the Nereids, sea nymphs noted for their beauty. The nymphs were offended and asked Poseidon, who was married to one of their number, to punish the vain Queen. He did so by sending Cetus (see page 78).

▼ One of Cassiopeia's most celebrated objects is all but invisible at optical wavelengths, even in large telescopes. It is Casssiopeia A, the remains of a supernova that happened long ago. At radio wavelengths, as here, Cas-A is one of the brightest objects in the heavens.

With its brightest stars aligned in a distinctive W-shape, Cassiopeia is unmistakable. It is a far northern constellation, located on the opposite side of the Pole Star from Ursa Major. From Canada, the northern United States and northern Europe, it is circumpolar and always visible.

Cassiopeia sits in the Milky Way, and the region is rich in clusters and dense star fields, which reward leisurely sweeping with binoculars.

The "W" stars

Alpha (Shedir), Beta and Gamma are almost identical in brightness (about magnitude 2.2). Alpha, the southernmost star of the "W", has a distinctly orange hue, compared with the pure white of Beta. Telescopes will resolve it into a double star, with the orange of the brilliant primary contrasting with the bluish white of the fainter companion.

Nearby Eta is another fine double star, with golden yellow and purplish components. The central star of the "W", Gamma, varies rather unpredictably. It is a very hot blue giant star that periodically throws off shells of luminous gas, causing its brightness to increase. In the 1930s, it rose to a magnitude of 1.6 to be the brightest star in the constellation, but later dipped to below 3.

Extending the "W" from Delta through Epsilon, you reach Iota. This is an excellent triple star for amateur telescopes.

Interesting variables

Continuing the same line through Iota brings you to RZ Cassiopeiae. This is an eclipsing binary variable star within binocular range. Usually of about the sixth magnitude, it falls nearly to the eighth when it is in eclipse, every 29 hours. The dimming can easily be followed because it takes place over just two hours.

On the other side of the constellation, beyond Beta, is a line of three stars, Tau, Rho and Sigma. The central star Rho is an irregular variable of unknown type, which fluctuates between about magnitudes 4 and 6 quite unpredictably. The fifth-magnitude flanking stars Tau and Sigma are useful for comparison.

A regular Mira-type variable, R Cassiopeiae, lies south of Rho, though it is not easy to find because of the dense star fields of the Milky Way. At full brightness it reaches the sixth magnitude, but fades to the thirteenth over a period of 431 days.

Fine clusters

Rich star fields lie around Epsilon, Delta and Gamma, together with a number of clusters. They include the open clusters NGC663, 654 and M103, the brightest. However, the open cluster NGC457, south of Delta and close to Phi, is a more interesting object. It is a compact group of more than 100 stars. Binoculars show it well, and small telescopes will resolve its stars.

Another open cluster worth observing is M52, found, though with some difficulty, by extending a line through Alpha and Beta. It is a cluster of about 100 hot young stars rather like the Pleiades. It is an excellent subject for the small telescope.

For information about surrounding constellations, see the following pages:
Andromeda 78   Cepheus 40

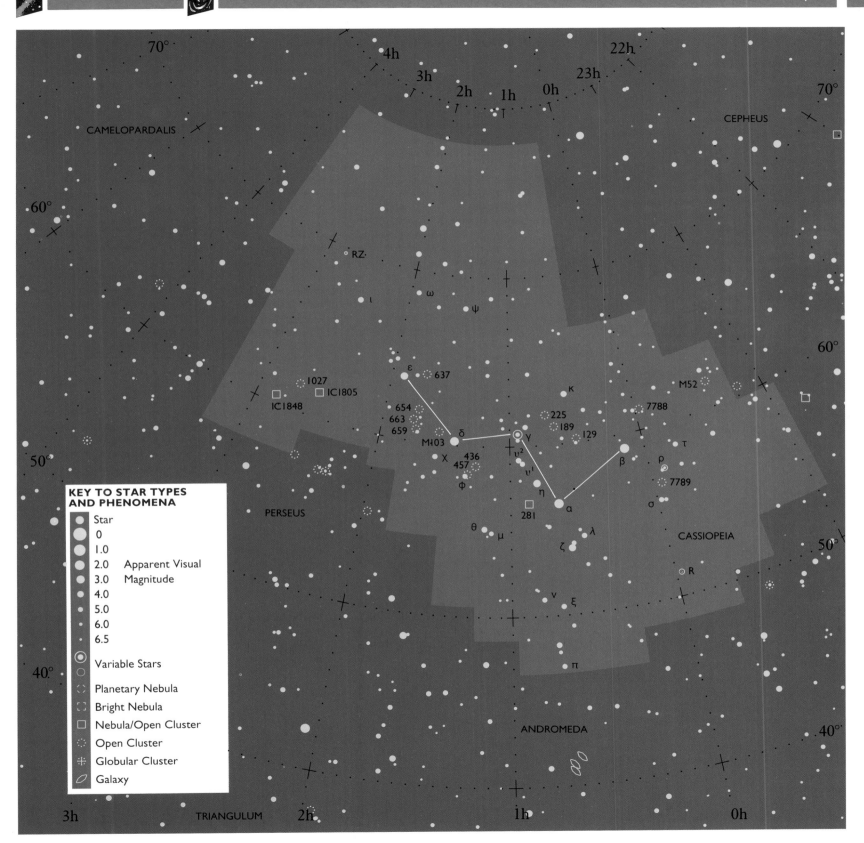

70°

4h 3h 2h 1h 0h 23h 22h

CAMELOPARDALIS

CEPHEUS

70°

60°

60°

RZ

ι ω ψ

50°

ε 637

1027

IC1805

IC1848

654
663
659

δ

M103

χ

436
457

φ

κ

225
189 129

γ

υ²

υ¹

η

281

M52

7788

τ

β ρ

7789

σ

CASSIOPEIA

50°

KEY TO STAR TYPES AND PHENOMENA

Star
0
1.0
2.0   Apparent Visual
3.0   Magnitude
4.0
5.0
6.0
6.5

⊙ Variable Stars

⟨⟩ Planetary Nebula

▱ Bright Nebula

□ Nebula/Open Cluster

⫶ Open Cluster

✳ Globular Cluster

⬭ Galaxy

PERSEUS

θ
μ

ζ

λ

R

ν ξ

40°

ANDROMEDA

40°

π

3h   TRIANGULUM   2h   1h   0h

CENTAURUS

Centaurus the Centaur was one of the mythical creatures that were half-man, half-horse. Mostly, centaurs were wild creatures, but this particular centaur was different. Named Chiron, he was wise and learned and became a great teacher, especially of hunting, healing and music. Despite his medical skills, he could not heal himself when he was accidentally hit by one of Hercules' poisoned arrows.

Centaurus is one of the largest constellations in the heavens, and is one of the most spectacular. It has its "feet" in the Milky Way and envelops the distinctive Crux, the Southern Cross.

Centaurus boasts the third brightest star in the night sky, the nearest star, a wealth of open and globular clusters and galaxies, and it contains one of the most intense radio sources in the sky.

The Alpha Centauri system

The leading star Alpha, sometimes called Rigil Kent, has a magnitude of −0.3 and is outshone in the heavens only by Sirius and Canopus. Alpha Centauri is a double star, separated in small telescopes into yellow components. It lies just 4.3 light years away, less than half the distance of Sirius.

When Alpha is viewed in large telescopes, a third faint star comes into view. It is a red dwarf of the eleventh magnitude, and it is closer even than Alpha. Indeed it is the nearest star to the Earth, and is appropriately called Proxima Centauri.

Beta, also called Agena, has a magnitude of 0.6. It forms a prominent pair with Alpha, and the two are called the Pointers because they point to the Southern Cross. Being bluish white, Beta contrasts with yellow Alpha. Though side by side in the heavens, the two are literally light years apart, more than 450 in fact.

Between the Pointers is the Mira-type variable R. It is an easy binocular subject at its maximum, when it is at the fifth magnitude, but fades to the eleventh at minimum over a period of 547 days.

Outstanding Omega

Following a line from Beta through Epsilon to an equal distance beyond brings you to yet another glorious feature of the southern skies. It looks like a fuzzy fourth-magnitude star and is labelled Omega.

However, Omega Centauri is not a star at all, but a grouping of hundreds of thousands of stars, maybe as many as a million! It is in fact the finest example of a globular cluster there is. It is readily visible to the naked eye, and even binoculars will begin to resolve its stars.

Another globular cluster worth investigating in binoculars and a small telescope is NGC5286, just north of Epsilon. One of the finest open clusters in the constellation is NGC3766, near Lambda on the opposite side of the Southern Cross from Alpha and Beta.

Crux, the Southern Cross

This, the smallest constellation, is circumpolar in New Zealand and much of Australia. Four main stars make up the Cross, Alpha (Acrux), Beta, Gamma and Delta. Warm reddish Gamma makes a nice contrast with the other bluish white stars. Alpha (magnitude 0.8) is a double, as are Beta and Gamma and the pair Theta.

Near Beta is Crux's finest gem, a beautiful coloured open cluster nicknamed the Jewel Box, but officially termed Kappa Crucis or NGC4755. It is a glittering spectacle as its name implies, featuring a prominent red supergiant that shines like a ruby.

Kappa Crucis lies at the edge of a dark "hole" in the Milky Way star fields, appropriately named the Coal Sack. It is, in fact, a large dark nebula.

▶ Stars beyond number cluster together in one of the finest sights in Centaurus, Omega Centauri. It is the largest, brightest and richest globular cluster in the heavens, occupying about the same area of the sky as the Full Moon. It lies about 17,000 light years away.

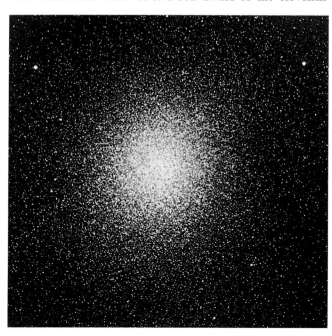

For information about surrounding constellations, see the following pages:

Carina 42   Hydra 50
Lupus 53

LIBRA

14h 13h CORVUS 12h

CRATER

−30°

CENTAURUS

HYDRA

−30°

θ

ι

ψ

−40°

ν

φ μ

η

5128

κ

υ¹

υ²

3680

−40°

ζ

5460

ω

τ

ξ²

ξ¹

γ

σ

5286

δ

ε

ρ

−50°

KEY TO STAR TYPES AND PHENOMENA

Star

0

1.0

2.0 Apparent Visual

3.0 Magnitude

4.0

5.0

6.0

6.5

Variable Stars

Planetary Nebula

Bright Nebula

Nebula/Open Cluster

Open Cluster

Globular Cluster

Galaxy

5662

5606 R

β

α 5617

5138

μ γ

λ β 4337

κ

4755 4439

4609 4349 4103

α

CRUX ζ θ

η

4463

5316

5281

3960

3918

ε

o

3766

λ

VELA

−50°

−60°

NORMA

CIRCINUS

MUSCA

CARINA

−60°

ARA

16h

TRIANGULUM AUS.

15h 14h 13h 12h 11h

CYGNUS

Cygnus the Swan is supposed to be Zeus (Jupiter), king of the gods, in disguise. Zeus assumed this form when visiting one of his many lady loves, Leda, Queen of Sparta. The result of the liaison was an egg, out of which hatched the twins Castor and Pollux and also Helen, who would become the beautiful Helen of Troy, with the "face that launched a thousand ships". Pollux and Helen were both Zeus's children, but Castor was not; he was the son of the King of Sparta.

▼ The delicate Veil Nebula (NGC6992), which is part of the extensive supernova remnant known as the Cygnus Loop. The name is a good one for these wispy threads of glowing gas, as is the alternative name, the Cirrus Nebula.

Cygnus is a beautiful northern constellation and one of the few to resemble the figure it is named for. The Swan is depicted flying south along the Milky Way. Cygnus's distinctive cross-shape gives it the alternative name of the Northern Cross.

Cygnus provides an astronomical feast. It features many fine doubles and variables. Being largely in the Milky Way, it also abounds in star fields and clusters, which put on a magnificent display in binoculars. Larger telescopes reveal magnificent nebulae and diaphanous wisps of glowing gas.

Dazzling Deneb

The leading star Alpha, or Deneb, in the Swan's tail, is of the first magnitude. It is exceptionally luminous, with the light output of more than 60,000 Suns. It lies very much farther away than all the other bright stars, at a distance of more than 1,800 light years. If the brightest star in the sky, Sirius, were at that distance, we would hardly notice it!

Deneb is one of the three bright stars that make up the Summer Triangle. The others are Altair in Aquila and Vega in Lyra.

Lovely doubles

Beta, or Albireo, is at the opposite end of Cygnus from Deneb and is much fainter (third magnitude). But viewed even through a small telescope it is a gem of a double, probably the loveliest in the sky. Its blue and yellow components always appear clear and bright.

Delta and Gamma are also double, as is 61, under the Swan's right "wing". 61 Cygni has a greater claim to fame than just being a double. It was the first star to have its distance measured accurately. The German astronomer Friedrich Bessel worked out the distance, by the parallax method, in 1838. It proved to be over 105 million million kilometres. That the stars were so remote caused a sensation.

Red variables

Cygnus contains several Mira-type variables, visible in binoculars at maximum brightness and worth viewing if only for their intense red colour. One of the most interesting is Chi, located in the Swan's neck. At maximum, Chi Cygni rivals the steady and nearby Eta (magnitude 3.6) in brightness. At minimum it fades to below magnitude 14 over a period of 407 days, thus displaying one of the greatest changes in brightness known among variables.

Other Mira variables include U and R Cygni which come within binocular range near maximum, but fade way beyond it for much of the time. U is east of the star 32, which is itself north of the pair Omicron 1 and 2 under the Swan's left wing. R is located close to Theta farther out.

W Cygni, on the opposite side of the constellation close to the fourth-magnitude Rho, is a semi-regular variable with a period of about four months. Its change in brightness, from the fifth to the eighth magnitude, keeps it within range of binoculars throughout its cycle.

Deep-sky revelations

In all there are up to 30 open clusters in the constellation, including two Messier clusters. M29 is located just south of Gamma; and M39 is found in the tail end of the constellation, forming a right-angled triangle with Pi-2 and Rho. M39 is the larger of the two, with more than 20 stars covering nearly half a Moon diameter.

Between Deneb and the much fainter Xi, the Milky Way noticeably brightens. Viewed through binoculars or a telescope, the region is revealed as a large nebula (NGC7000). Long-exposure photographs show a distinctive shape that gives it the name of the North America Nebula.

South of Epsilon in the Swan's right wing is a fourth-magnitude star 52. When the region is viewed in large binoculars or a telescope, filaments of glowing gas show up. And long-exposure photographs reveal a delicate looping tracery known as the Cygnus Loop. It is a supernova remnant, the remains of a supernova explosion that happened maybe 30,000 years ago. We know a bright part of the Loop as the Veil Nebula, sometimes called the Cirrus Nebula.

For information about surrounding constellations, see the following pages:

Cassiopeia 80	Cepheus 40
Draco 40	Lyra 56
Pegasus 62	

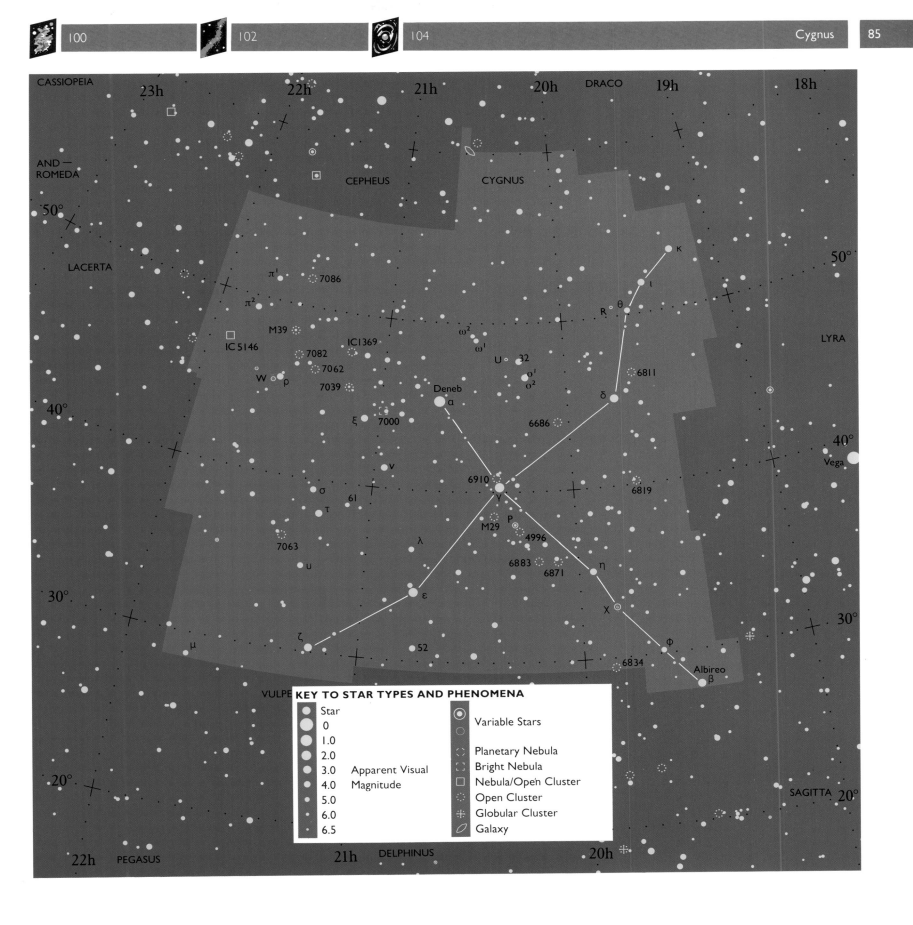

CASSIOPEIA
23h   22h   21h   20h   DRACO   19h   18h

AND —
ROMEDA

CEPHEUS   CYGNUS

50°   50°

LACERTA   κ
ι
LYRA
R   θ
π¹   7086   ω²
π²   ω¹
M39   U   32
IC 5146   IC 1369   o¹   6811
7082   o²
W   ρ   7062   δ
7039   Deneb   6686
α
40°   ξ   7000   40°
Vega
ν
σ   6910   6819
61   γ
τ   P   Vega
M29
7063   λ   4996
u   6883   η
6871
30°   ε   χ   30°
ζ   φ
μ   52   6834   Albireo
β

VULPE   **KEY TO STAR TYPES AND PHENOMENA**
○ Star
○ 0
○ 1.0   ◉ Variable Stars
○ 2.0   ◎
○ 3.0   ◇ Planetary Nebula
○ 4.0   Apparent Visual   ▢ Bright Nebula
○ 5.0   Magnitude   □ Nebula/Open Cluster
○ 6.0   ⊙ Open Cluster
· 6.5   ✦ Globular Cluster
⬭ Galaxy

20°   20°
SAGITTA

22h   21h   DELPHINUS   20h
PEGASUS

ORION

In mythology Orion was a mighty hunter. He was the son of the sea god Poseidon, who gave him the power to walk on the sea. Orion features in many tales. In one he fell in love with seven sisters, the Pleiades, and pursued them, as he does still in the heavens. Different stories tell of how Orion died. One tells of Orion's boast that he could kill any creature alive, which caused the Earth to open. Out came a scorpion, which promptly stung him to death.

The celestial equator passes through this magnificent constellation, which is therefore equally familiar to sky-watchers in both hemispheres.

"Magnificent" is certainly the right word to describe Orion, whose main pattern of bright stars makes it one of the most readily recognizable of all the constellations. Also, its outline really does look like the figure it is meant to represent, the mighty hunter with club upraised and shield at the ready.

Twin giants
Two stars vie with each other to be the finest in the constellation, Alpha, or Betelgeux (sometimes spelt Betelgeuse and pronounced "beetle-juice"), and Beta, or Rigel.

Betelgeux is supergigantic; if it were where the Sun is, its globe would reach beyond the Earth's orbit nearly to Mars. It is obviously red and variable. At maximum brightness, it reaches a magnitude of 0.5, but can fade below 1 over an irregular period of about five to six years.

Rigel, which is diametrically opposite Betelgeux in the main star pattern, is actually brighter, shining steadily at magnitude 0.1. It differs too in colour, being bluish white. It is an intensely hot star with the energy output of more than 50,000 Suns. Larger telescopes will show it to be a double.

The other bright stars in Orion are also named: Gamma – Bellatrix, Delta – Mintaka, Epsilon – Alnilam, Zeta – Alnitak and Kappa – Saiph.

Great nebulae
Apart from the main star pattern, the most conspicuous feature of the constellation to the naked eye is a misty patch below the three stars, Delta, Epsilon and Zeta, which form Orion's Belt. Binoculars show it to be a bright nebula, M42, aptly named the Great Nebula in Orion. Long-exposure photographs of the nebula are needed to bring out its staggering beauty, which few other heavenly sights can match.

A much smaller, nearly round nebula, M43, lies close to the Great Nebula. There is a small reddish nebula close to Zeta, identified as NGC2024, and a slightly brighter and more bluish one farther north, M78.

South of Zeta is the glowing nebula IC434, which has obscuring dark matter silhouetted against it in the shape of a horse's head. This Horsehead Nebula, also called Barnard 33, is the most distinctive dark nebula in the heavens. Unfortunately, it is beyond the reach of smaller telescopes.

The nebulae highlighted above are really the "tip of the iceberg" because virtually the whole constellation sits in a tenuous gas cloud. It is this vast reservoir of interstellar matter that spawned hot white stars like Rigel and those in Orion's Belt.

Multiple choice
Orion is rich too in double and multiple stars. Pride of place must go to the star Theta Orionis, which is embedded in the Great Nebula. Called the Trapezium after the arrangement of its four components, it can be separated in small telescopes. It is the light from these that illuminates the Nebula. Iota, at the southern edge of the Nebula, is also double.

Going northwards, Sigma appears double in binoculars, but small telescopes reveal it as a triple, with white, bluish and reddish components. Larger instruments separate a fourth component. In Orion's Belt, Zeta and Delta are double. So is Lambda, the third-magnitude star marking Orion's "eye".

And Orion has still more to offer, in the way of variables, open clusters and planetary nebulae. Perhaps the easiest variable to find is the very red W, at the southern end of the arc of the six Pi stars that form Orion's Shield. W is a long-period variable of the Mira type, which varies between about the sixth and eighth magnitudes over a period of 212 days and is always within binocular range.

The open cluster NGC2169 is the brightest in the constellation at about the eighth magnitude. It forms an equilateral triangle with Xi and Nu in Orion's upraised right hand. Going farther north, NGC2174/5 is an attractive combination open cluster and nebula, in line with Chi 1 and 2.

▲ Our telescopes reveal that Orion contains many fine nebulae, notably M42. But the infrared astronomy satellite IRAS revealed that gas and dust pervade practically the whole of the constellation. This IRAS image highlights this vast region of interstellar matter. Alpha (Betelgeux) is pinpointed.

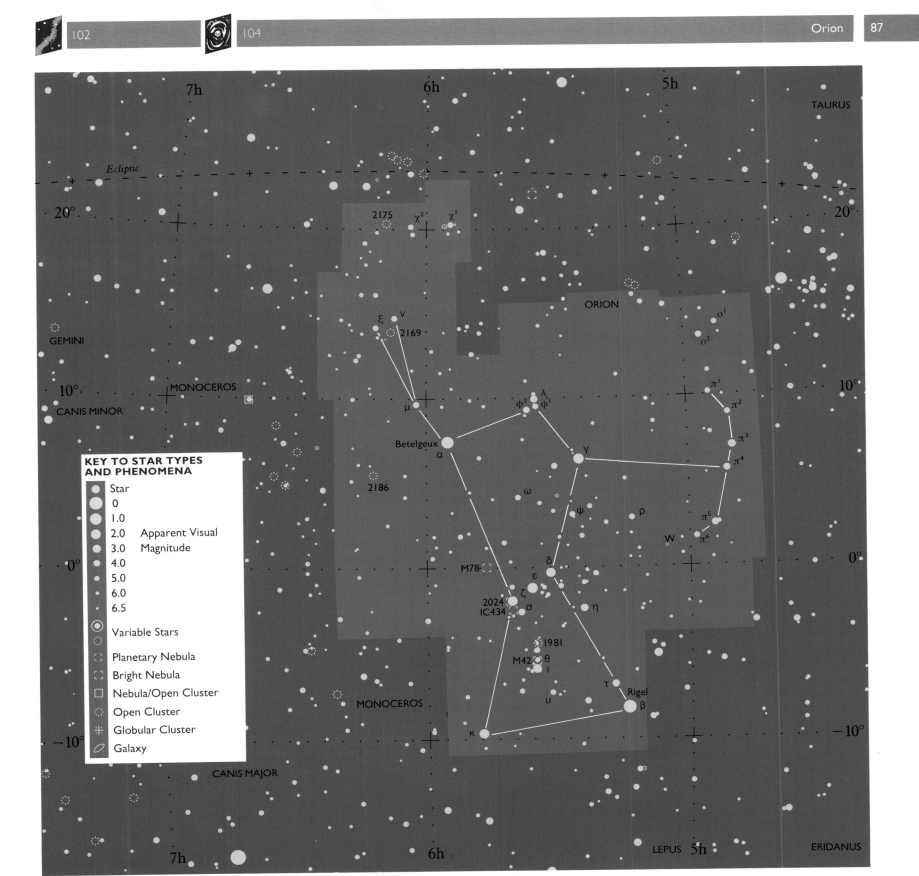

Ecliptic

20° 20°

2175 χ² χ¹

ORION

GEMINI

ν ξ ν o¹
2169 o²

10° MONOCEROS 10°

CANIS MINOR

μ π¹
φ² λ π²
Betelgeux φ¹
α γ π³

π⁴
2186
ω
ψ ρ
π⁵

W π⁶

**KEY TO STAR TYPES
AND PHENOMENA**

Star
0
1.0
2.0   Apparent Visual
3.0   Magnitude
4.0
5.0
6.0
6.5

δ

0° ε 0°
M78

2024 ζ
IC434 σ η

◉ Variable Stars

○

⬙ Planetary Nebula
1981

⬚ Bright Nebula M42 θ

□ Nebula/Open Cluster ι τ
Rigel
⬚ Open Cluster υ β

✳ Globular Cluster

⬭ Galaxy MONOCEROS

κ

-10° -10°

CANIS MAJOR

SAGITTARIUS

Sagittarius the Archer is depicted as a half-man, half-horse centaur, but one of the warlike ones (unlike Centaurus, page 82). He has his bow drawn, with the arrow pointing to Antares, the Scorpion's heart.

In early times Sagittarius was thought of rather as a satyr, a two-legged creature that was half-man, half-goat. He was identified with Crotus, the inventor of archery, whose father was the pipe-playing god Pan.

Sagittarius is one of the richest constellations in the heavens, spanning the Milky Way. The Milky Way here is magnificent, studded with clusters and beautiful nebulae and brilliant with dense star clouds. The densest mark the direction of the centre of our Galaxy some 30,000 light years away. Swept with binoculars, this part of the night sky takes the breath away.

Alas for most skywatchers in the Northern Hemisphere, Sagittarius never rises high enough to be fully appreciated. How they envy astronomers down under!

A Messier feast

The constellation has a number of double and variable stars (such as the Cepheid variable W, close to Gamma). However, its chief attraction lies in its deep-sky objects. Charles Messier catalogued more of them in Sagittarius than in any other constellation, including some of the best-known nebulae and many globular clusters.

M8, the Lagoon Nebula, is one of the brightest of the Messier nebulae. Of the fifth magnitude, it can be glimpsed with the naked eye, making a triangle with Lambda and Mu. It is a fine object in binoculars and a

small telescope but, as always with nebulae, only long-exposure photographs bring out its full beauty. Such pictures show up dark gas lanes and many tiny black condensations known as Bok globules, which are probably on the way to becoming stars.

Just to the north of M8 is an equally famous nebula, M20, the Trifid. This is visible in binoculars as a small misty patch. Telescopes will reveal its three dark dust lanes, which give the nebula its name.

The third major nebula in Sagittarius, M17, is located at the northern border of the constellation on the edge of the Milky Way. It is probably best found by following a line between Gamma Scuti in the neighbouring constellation and Mu. M17 has roughly the shape of the Greek letter omega, and so is usually called the Omega Nebula. It has the alternative names of the Swan and the Horseshoe Nebula.

Cluster collection

Immediately south of the Omega Nebula is the open cluster M18 and south of this M24. M24 is neither a nebula nor a cluster but a general brightening of the Milky Way, and is otherwise known as the Small Sagittarius Star Cloud.

Making a triangle with M24 and Mu is a good binocular open cluster M23, a collection of over 100 stars of up to the ninth magnitude. Farther south, near the Trifid Nebula, is a similar object M21.

Great globulars

Sagittarius boasts more than 20 globular clusters, about one-tenth of the number known. That it contains so many is not really surprising, because globulars tend to congregate around the centres of galaxies.

The top globular is undoubtedly M22, which forms a triangle with Lambda and Phi. M22 is a dense grouping of literally millions of stars. It rates the sixth magnitude and is just visible to the naked eye. It looks great in binoculars and small telescopes, which begin to resolve its outer stars.

Other notable globulars include M54 and M55. M54 is located close to Zeta, while M55 is at about the same declination some way to the east. M55 is a much looser condensation of stars, counted in thousands rather than millions like M22.

▲ One of the dense star clouds in Sagittarius, looking towards the centre of the Galaxy. This region is a delight for binocular observers.

▶ The Lagoon Nebula (M8) is named because of the shape of the dark lane running through it. It is a vast object, maybe as much as 100 light years across. It lies about 5,000 light years away.

For information about surrounding constellations, see the following pages:

Aquila	58	Capricornus	58
Ophiuchus	56	Scorpius	90
Scutum	57	Serpens Cauda	57

AQUILA
20h
19h
SCUTUM
18h
OPHIUCHUS

−10°

CAPRICORNUS
SAGITTARIUS
SERPENS (Cauda)

6822
υ
M17
M18
6645
6716
M24
M23
υ
ξ¹
6595
ϱ¹
M25
μ
ϱ²
π
o
ξ²
M21
6469
ν²
ν¹
6456
M20
Ecliptic
−20°
6530
6553
M22
6642
6544 M8
ψ
λ
M28
6523
σ
φ
6520
ω
τ
δ
W 6528
ζ
6624
γ
M54
M70
M69
6569
M55
M52
6723
ε
θ²
θ¹
η
SCORPIUS
MICROSCOPIUM

−30°

−40°
ι
κ¹
α
κ²
CORONA
AUSTRALIS
β

INDUS
21h
20h
19h
TELESCOPIUM
18h
ARA 17h

KEY TO STAR TYPES AND PHENOMENA

Star	⊚ Variable Stars
0	○
1.0	
2.0	⬦ Planetary Nebula
3.0	⬚ Bright Nebula
4.0 Apparent Visual	☐ Nebula/Open Cluster
5.0 Magnitude	⬚ Open Cluster
6.0	✳ Globular Cluster
6.5	⬭ Galaxy

SCORPIUS

Scorpius the Scorpion was the creature that stung to death the mighty hunter Orion. Orion and Scorpius were therefore placed on opposite sides of the heavens, so that Orion disappears as the Scorpion rises. In the sky, however, Scorpius itself is threatened by Sagittarius the Archer, whose arrow is pointing at the Scorpion's heart, marked by Antares. The constellation that is now Libra once formed the Scorpion's front claws.

▲ The whole constellation of Scorpius, photographed by the author in the Australian Outback under perfect seeing conditions. It was taken by a tripod-mounted 35-mm camera with standard lens. The exposure time was about half a minute on Ektachrome 400 film "pushed" to 800. It demonstrates that reasonable night-sky pictures can be obtained even with simple photographic equipment.

Scorpius is another of those southern constellations that are the envy of northern astronomers. It is relatively small, but brilliant, boasting no less than 11 stars above the third magnitude. Also, practically all of the constellation lies within the Milky Way, and in one of the richest parts of it too, where open and globular clusters abound.

The name given to the constellation is, for a change, appropriate. Only the slightest imagination is required to picture a scorpion poised to strike, with head in the north of the constellation and its curved tail, with deadly sting, in the south.

Rival of Mars

Scorpius's brightest star is Alpha, or Antares, which marks the heart of the Scorpion. Its name means "rival of Mars", alluding to its resemblance to the Red Planet. It is perhaps the reddest of the bright stars, more so than

Betelgeux, for example.

Like Betelgeux, Antares is a red supergiant, but it is even bigger, probably as much as 700 times the size of the Sun. If it were where the Sun is, its surface would stretch beyond the orbit of Mars up to the asteroid belt.

Being so large, Antares is unstable and pulsates, changing in brightness slightly as it does so and averaging about magnitude 1.

The Scorpion's "head"

An arc of four stars, Nu, Beta, Delta and Pi, mark the Scorpion's "head". In the present constellation, the claws are missing, the claw stars now forming part of the neighbouring constellation Libra.

Of the "head" stars, Nu appears double in binoculars, and telescopes show each component itself to be double, making Nu a quadruple system. Second-magnitude Beta is also a fine double star with bluish white components. Nearby Omega is an easy binocular double.

Moving south along the "backbone" of bright stars, Sigma is double (as, incidentally, is Antares). Mu and Zeta, at the base of the "tail", are wide, easy doubles. Zeta 1, the brighter component, is reddish orange, Zeta 2 is bluish white. In binoculars or a small telescope, the region around Zeta is fascinating. It includes the third-magnitude open cluster NGC6231 composed, like the Pleiades, of young hot stars and plainly visible to the naked eye.

Sting in the tail

The tail region of Scorpius is also a delight for naked-eye skywatcher, binocular viewer and small-telescope observer alike. Lambda, or Shaula, at magnitude 1.6, marks the Scorpion's sting. It is only fractionally brighter than Theta farther south.

M7 and M6 are bright open clusters visible to the naked eye north of the tail. Both can be resolved into stars in binoculars. The third-magnitude M7 is the brighter and larger of the two, covering an area of sky larger than that of the full moon. M6 is also known as the Butterfly Cluster, because of the "open-wing" arrangement of its principal stars.

Other Messier objects in the constellation include the sixth-magnitude M4 right next to Antares, a fine globular cluster for small telescopes. M80 is a somewhat fainter globular roughly midway between Antares and Beta.

For information about surrounding constellations, see the following pages:

Ara	42	Libra	53
Lupus	53	Ophiuchus	56
Sagittarius	88	Serpens Cauda	57

KEY TO STAR TYPES AND PHENOMENA

Star
0
1.0
2.0
3.0   Apparent Visual
4.0   Magnitude
5.0
6.0
6.5

Variable Stars

Planetary Nebula
Bright Nebula
Nebula/Open Cluster
Open Cluster
Globular Cluster
Galaxy

TAURUS

Taurus the Bull was one of the many disguises adopted by king-of-the-gods Zeus on his amorous adventures. Zeus assumed the form of a magnificent snow-white beast with shining horns when he set out to woo the fair Europa. He encouraged her to climb on his back, then carried her off to the island of Crete. There he revealed his true self. One of their children was King Minos, who built the palace of Knossos.

This large constellation adjoins Orion and, as far as stars are concerned, it is faint by comparison, but it boasts a fine leading star which marks the "eye" of the Bull, two of the brightest open clusters in the heavens and the best-known supernova remnant.

The leading star is Alpha, or Aldebaran, which is easily found by following a line through Orion's Belt towards the northwest. Aldebaran is unmistakable both because of its brightness (magnitude 0.8) and its lovely orange colour. It is similar in brightness and appearance to Betelgeux in Orion, not far away.

Beta, or Al Nath, is the second brightest star (magnitude 1.6), and marks the tip of one of the Bull's horns. Third-magnitude Zeta marks the tip of the other. Both Beta and Zeta lie on the edge of the Milky Way.

Among the other stars, Lambda is worth watching because it is an eclipsing binary of the Algol type. Every four days, its brightness dips momentarily from the third to the fourth magnitude as the dim star of the pair passes in front of the bright one.

The Hyades

Close to Aldebaran lies a scattered group of stars which form a distinctive V-shape and which are clearly visible to the naked eye. Known as the Hyades, they form one of the finest open clusters in the night sky.

The brightest star in the Hyades is Theta, a naked-eye double consisting of a white primary of magnitude 3.4 and a slightly fainter orange companion. Binoculars show the colour difference well. Several of the other stars in the cluster are of similar brightness, including Epsilon, Delta and Gamma. Delta forms a double with a fainter star 64 Tauri. Sigma is another double close to Aldebaran.

Under good viewing conditions, as many as 20 stars can be detected in the Hyades with the naked eye. This is about one-tenth of the total number of stars in the cluster. On average, the Hyades lies about 130 light years away, making it one of the nearest open clusters. Aldebaran

itself is not part of the group, being only about half the distance away.

Seven Sisters

North-west of the Hyades lies an even more spectacular cluster, M45 or the Pleiades. It is also called the Seven Sisters because keen-sighted people should be able to spot at least seven of its brightest stars with the naked eye. Binoculars and telescopes reveal more and more stars, which probably number in total more than 300.

Compared with the Hyades, the Pleiades is much more concentrated and thus more brilliant, shining nearly as brightly as a first-magnitude star. It differs from the Hyades in several other ways. It is much farther away, at about 400 light years, and it is much younger. Whereas the Hyades stars are on average about 400 million years old, those in the Pleiades are youngsters of 10–20 million years old. They are hot and white, and surrounded by nebulosity, which becomes visible in photographs.

The brightest Pleiades star is Alcyone (magnitude 2.9), and in descending order of brightness come the other six of the "Seven Sisters": Atlas, Electra, Maia, Merope, Taygete and Pleione.

The Crab

Close by Zeta, at the tip of the Bull's southern horn, is another of Taurus's great sights, M1, the Crab Nebula. It is a supernova remnant, an expanding cloud of writhing gas that resulted from a supernova explosion. It is one of the few whose precise age we know. The supernova was witnessed in July AD 1054 by Chinese astronomers, who recorded that it was so bright that it was visible in daylight for several weeks.

The Crab is just visible in powerful binoculars, and in small telescopes appears as an oval glow. Larger telescopes are required for closer study. They bring out bright interlacing filaments which appear red in long-exposure photographs.

The Nebula was named, incidentally, in 1844 by the English astronomer, the third Earl of Rosse, but it had been discovered over a century earlier. It was the first sight of the Nebula by the French astronomer Charles Messier in 1758 that inspired him to begin his historic catalogue of nebulous objects. This explains why the Crab Nebula is M1.

▲ This is the famous Crab Nebula, the still-expanding cloud of gas that was blasted into space from a supernova in AD 1054. At the heart of the Crab is a tiny rotating neutron star, or pulsar, which flashes pulses of energy towards us 30 times a second.

AURIGA 6h 5h 4h PERSEUS 3h

30° 30°

ARIES

GEMINI β

ψ

φ

χ M45
Pleiades

1746

MI ι

τ

20° 20°

ζ ε

1647

δ

1817 1807 α

ORION Aldebaran θ Hyades

σ 71 γ

ρ π

90 λ

ξ

88 10° 10°

CETUS

Betelgeux

μ

ν

ERIDANUS

KEY TO STAR TYPES AND PHENOMENA

Star
0 ◉ Variable Stars
1.0 ○
2.0 ⬦ Planetary Nebula
3.0 Apparent Visual ⬚ Bright Nebula
4.0 Magnitude ▫ Nebula/Open Cluster
5.0 ⦿ Open Cluster
6.0 ✳ Globular Cluster
6.5 ⬭ Galaxy

0° 0°

6h 5h 4h

URSA MAJOR

Ursa Major the Great Bear is usually associated with the huntress Callisto, a favourite of Artemis, the goddess of hunting. One day Zeus, cunningly assuming the guise of Artemis, lay with Callisto and made her pregnant. She bore a son, Arcas. Zeus's wife Hera was not amused and turned Callisto into a bear. Later, Zeus placed Callisto in the heavens as the Great Bear, to prevent her being killed by her son, who came upon her when hunting.

The third largest constellation, Ursa Major occupies a vast region of far northern skies. It is circumpolar for northern Europe, Canada and the northern United States. Even though it does not boast any stars of the first magnitude, it is the best-known constellation in the Northern Hemisphere. This is because of the distinctive pattern made by seven bright second- and third-magnitude stars which stands out clearly in an otherwise relatively dark area of sky.

This pattern is known as the Plough or, in North America, the Big Dipper. It is called the Plough because of its resemblance to the handle and ploughshare of an old horse-drawn plough; the Big Dipper because of its resemblance to a ladle.

It should be emphasized that the Plough itself is not a constellation, but represents just the "tail" and "hindquarters" of the Bear. It occupies only a small part of the whole constellation of Ursa Major.

Following the Plough

As might be expected in such a prominent pattern, the stars all have names. Alpha is named Dubhe, Beta is Merak, Gamma is Phad, Delta is Megrez, Epsilon is Alioth, Zeta is Mizar and Eta is Alkaid.

The Alpha-to-Eta designation in this instance does not give the order of brightness of the stars. In fact Epsilon vies with Alpha to be the brightest star, both having a magnitude of 1.8. Eta runs them a close third, followed by Zeta. Delta is the dimmest of the seven, at magnitude 3.3.

Perhaps the most interesting of the Plough stars is Mizar (Zeta), marking the bend in the Plough's handle. Mizar is a complex multiple star. To begin with, it is a naked-eye double, whose companion is a fourth-magnitude star named Alchor. Seen through a small telescope, Mizar itself is seen to be double, and examination of the spectra of the two components reveals that they are both close binary systems.

▲ M101 is a striking galaxy of the Sc type, with open and well-defined spiral arms. Its apt popular name is the Pinwheel Galaxy. It is one of the largest spirals known, and is twice as big across as our own Galaxy.

Pointing north

Dubhe (Alpha) differs from the other stars in the Plough, which are white, by having a pronounced orange hue. It and Merak (Beta) are known as the Pointers, because a line drawn northwards through them points to Polaris, the Pole Star.

For this reason, the Plough has been a boon to navigators in the Northern Hemisphere for centuries, but it will not always be so. Dubhe and Alkaid (Eta) are moving in different directions from the other stars in the Plough. So Merak and Dubhe will end up pointing in quite a different direction.

Variables

Ursa Major has a number of variables that are binocular subjects. They include two long-period variables of the Mira-type: R, north of Dubhe; and T, which makes an equilateral triangle with Epsilon and Delta. They both vary from a respectable magnitude 6.7 down to beyond 13. R has a period of 301 days; T a period of 265 days.

Z, west of Delta, is a semi-regular variable, which always stays within binocular range, varying between magnitudes 7 and 9 in about 200 days.

A fine pair

Ursa Major is a region of the sky that is well endowed with galaxies, many of them within reach of amateur telescopes and a few within reach of binoculars. The two brightest are a close pair, M81 and M82, which appear to be physically associated, or "interacting". They are perhaps best found from Dubhe and 23, with which they form a right-angled triangle. These two galaxies form part of a small cluster that lies relatively close to Earth, only about 8 million light years away.

M81 is a classic spiral galaxy not dissimilar to our own, and bright at a magnitude of about 7. M82 is somewhat fainter and irregular in shape. It is a powerful radio source, which indicates that some almighty upheaval is occurring inside it.

Another galaxy of interest is the eighth-magnitude M101. It is a large spiral seen face-on, located north of the handle of the Plough, and forms an equilateral triangle with Eta and Mizar. Large telescopes are needed to identify the spiral arms and to bring out nebulae therein. Among other galaxies relatively easy to find are K109, close to Gamma, and M108, close to Merak. Just south of M108 is a fine planetary nebula, M97, called the Owl.

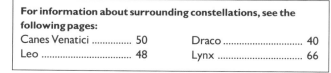

For information about surrounding constellations, see the following pages:

| Canes Venatici | 50 | Draco | 40 |
| Leo | 48 | Lynx | 66 |

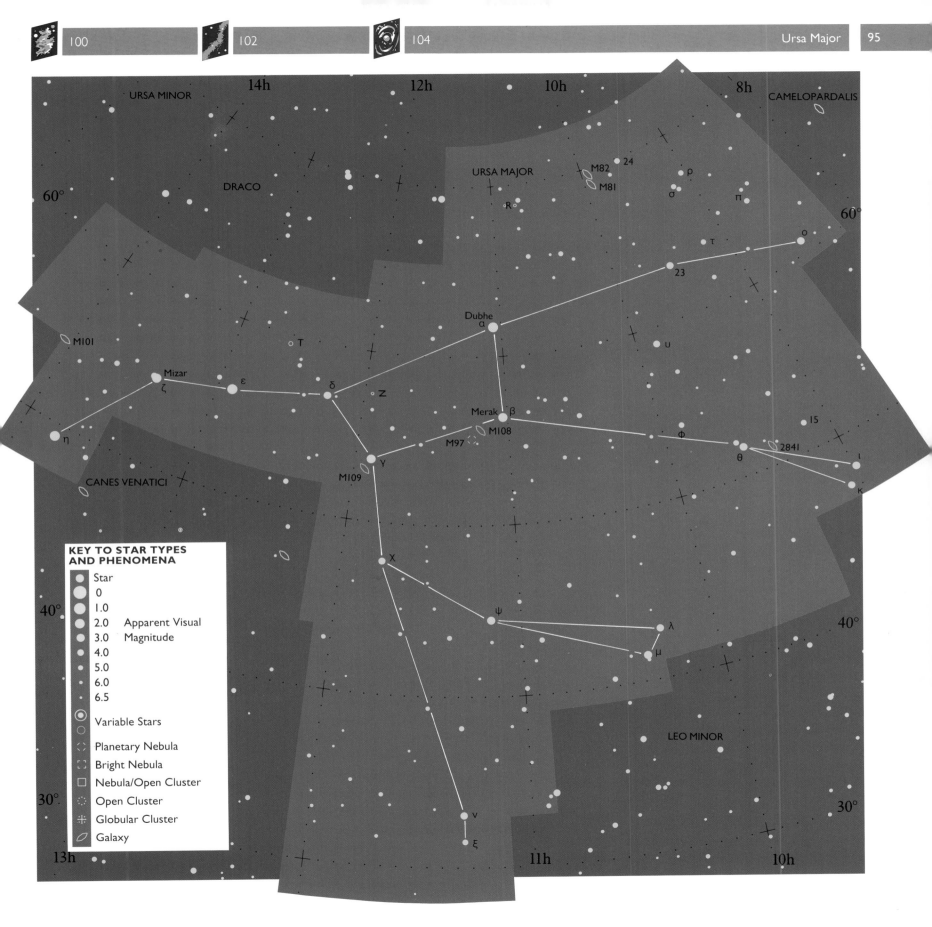

URSA MINOR

14h

12h

10h

8h

CAMELOPARDALIS

DRACO

60°

60°

URSA MAJOR

M82 24

M81 ρ

σ

π

R

τ

o

23

Dubhe
α

u

M101

Mizar

T

Z

15

ζ ε δ

Merak β

Φ

2841

M108

θ

M97

η

M109 γ

ι

CANES VENATICI

κ

KEY TO STAR TYPES
AND PHENOMENA

Star

0

1.0

2.0   Apparent Visual

3.0   Magnitude

4.0

5.0

6.0

6.5

40°

χ

40°

ψ

λ

Variable Stars

μ

Planetary Nebula

Bright Nebula

Nebula/Open Cluster

LEO MINOR

Open Cluster

Globular Cluster

Galaxy

30°

30°

ν

13h

ξ

11h

10h

VIRGO

Virgo the Virgin represents the goddess of justice Astraea in Greek and Roman mythology. Earlier she was the goddess Ishtar in Babylon and Isis in Egypt. Astraea is depicted with wings, with which she flew into the heavens when she despaired of the human race. In her left hand she holds an ear of wheat, marked by Spica.

Virgo spans the celestial equator and covers a vast region of the heavens. It is very nearly the largest constellation, second only to Hydra. It has a discernible Y-shape, but to see any resemblance to a maiden, with or without angel wings, requires considerable imagination.

To the naked eye Virgo is disappointing, since it has only one really bright star. However, telescopes reveal the constellation to be crammed with deep-sky objects, particularly galaxies. They form part of a huge cluster that extends into Coma Berenices.

Virgo's brightest star is Alpha, or Spica, whose magnitude is exactly 1. It is bluish white and is actually a binary, although this can only be detected from its spectrum.

Gamma and Epsilon are the next brightest stars, each of magnitude 2.8. Gamma is also a binary, with twin yellowish components (magnitude 3.6), which can be separated by small telescopes. The third-magnitude Delta, between Gamma and Epsilon, is noticeably reddish, as is Nu, north of Beta. Both Delta and Nu are red giants.

The Virgo Cluster

Extending right through the constellation, from south of Spica to the west of Epsilon, is a broad band of sky containing literally thousands of galaxies. They make up the celebrated Virgo Cluster.

This band of galaxies extends well into the neighbouring constellation, Coma Berenices. The whole system, called the Coma-Virgo Cluster, contains at least 3,000 galaxies. It is one of the largest of the many groupings of galaxies that populate the Universe and also one of the nearest. The closest galaxies lie about 40 million light years away, the farthest ones about 70 million light years.

A number of the galaxies in the Virgo Cluster are bright enough to be visible in small telescopes, and a few may even be glimpsed with powerful binoculars. Most, however, require large telescopes for detection or for bringing out any structure.

The Messier galaxies

The French astronomer Charles Messier catalogued many of the brighter galaxies (averaging about the ninth magnitude) and these are worth pursuing. Several are to be found in the region between Epsilon Virginis and Beta Leonis. In order they are M60, M59, M58, M89, M90, M87, M84 and M86.

M60 and M59 are a close pair of elliptical galaxies due north of the fifth-magnitude Rho. M58, slightly to the west, is a barred-spiral galaxy. The elliptical M89 and spiral M90 lie to the north of M58, and M87 lies to the west. The close pair M84 and M86, both ellipticals, appear in the same telescopic field of view north of M87.

Among these galaxies, M87 is outstanding in more ways than one. It is a giant elliptical galaxy, which is nearly spherical; its diameter is similar to that of our own galaxy, about 120,000 light years, but our galaxy is essentially a disc, so the near-spherical M87 contains very many more stars. Indeed, it is one of the most massive galaxies known and is a powerful source of radio waves.

Another interesting Messier galaxy, M104, an edge-on spiral, is found right on the border with Corvus, due south of Chi. It is of the eighth magnitude and may just be glimpsed in binoculars. Larger telescopes or long-exposure photographs are needed to bring out the dark dust lane that cuts through the oval image, giving it the vague appearance of a hat. This is why it is known as the Sombrero Galaxy.

Quasar quest

Beyond the range of small telescopes, but detectable with large ones, is an object called 3C373, located at the corner of a right-angled triangle with Gamma and Eta Virginis. It is a quasar and is of great historical interest and importance.

3C273 was the first quasar to be recognized as such, in 1962. A very remote star-like object with an incredible energy output, it shines at about the thirteenth magnitude, yet it is over 3,000 million light years away. No ordinary galaxies would show up at such a distance.

▲ The galaxy M87, which may perhaps contain as many as 3 million million stars, 30 times as many as our own Galaxy. This near-spherical object is one of the most notable "active" galaxies, pouring out enormous energy, particularly at radio and X-ray wavelengths.

For information about surrounding constellations, see the following pages:
Boötes 52   Coma Berenices 52
Hydra .... 48, 50   Leo 48
Libra 53

STAR CLUSTERS

As we observed in an earlier chapter, stars are gregarious and tend to travel through space with one or more companions. Sometimes they form part of much larger groupings of stars which we call clusters.

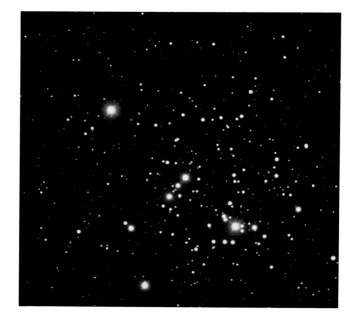

▲ This fine open cluster in Crux is NGC4755, popularly called the Jewel Box. It is often named the Kappa Crucis cluster after its central bright red star.

The most prominent cluster in the Northern Hemisphere is the Pleiades, or Seven Sisters, in Taurus. In the Southern Hemisphere the most prominent cluster is Omega Centauri, in Centaurus. But these two clusters are fundamentally different. The Pleiades is a fairly loose grouping of stars known as an open, or galactic cluster. Omega Centauri is a densely packed "globe" of stars known as a globular cluster.

Open clusters

We can see up to seven stars in the Pleiades with the naked eye (hence its popular name), but binoculars or a small telescope will reveal that it consists of many more stars. Altogether it contains several hundred, and this number is typical of an open cluster.

Although the stars in the Pleiades appear to be close together, they are in fact quite far apart. The whole cluster occupies a region about 15 light years across.

▼ The Pleiades, or Seven Sisters, one of the two striking clusters in Taurus. It is easily seen with the naked eye and looks glorious in binoculars. Its brightest star, Alcyone (in the centre of the picture), is just above the third magnitude.

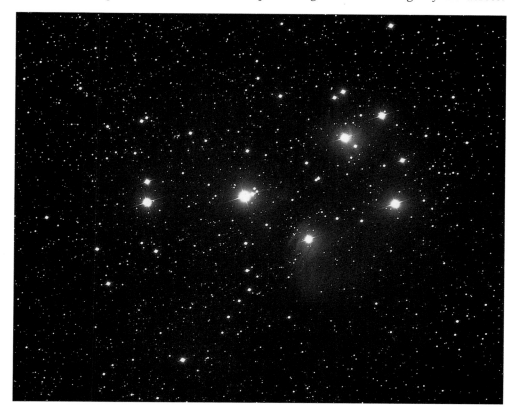

Long-exposure photographs of the Pleiades reveal that the bright stars are surrounded by a diffuse gas cloud, or nebulosity. This is typical of open clusters, which are usually made up of young, hot stars.

Taurus is also the home of another easily seen open cluster, the Hyades. This conglomeration of stars forms a V-shape around the brilliant orange Aldebaran, although this star is not part of the cluster – it is very much closer to us. The Hyades itself is one of the closest open clusters. About 140 light years away, it is only a quarter of the distance to the Pleiades.

Several other open clusters make rewarding viewing, among them M44 in Cancer. It is named Praesepe, or the Beehive, because it has been likened to a swarm of bees buzzing around a hive. Perseus boasts a close pair of open clusters, the famous Double Cluster (right), which looks magnificent in binoculars. In far southern skies is the incomparable Jewel Box in Crux (above), which lies close to the dark nebula we call the Coal Sack. Another southern cluster is M11 in Scutum, whose wing-shaped arrangement has earned it the name of the Wild Duck.

Globular clusters

The globular cluster Omega Centauri (page 82) could not be more different from the Pleiades open cluster. It consists of literally hundreds of thousands of stars packed together in a region of space only about 60 light years across. To the eye, it looks like one bright star, which is

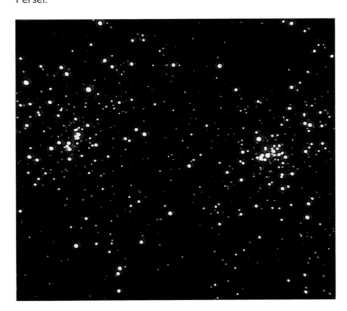

The distinctive Double Cluster in Perseus, also called the Sword Handle. These two clusters are naked-eye objects, designated h (left) and Chi Persei.

◄ The globular cluster M3 in Canes Venatici. One of the top globulars in northern skies, it is just beyond naked-eye range, but an easy binocular subject. Small telescopes will begin to resolve the outer fringes of this globe of some 45,000 stars. Like most globulars, M3 is remote, lying over 40,000 light years away.

why it was given a star name. But binoculars will start to reveal individual stars in the outer regions, and telescopes will resolve a host more.

Omega Centauri differs from the Pleiades in many other respects. For example, it lies 40 times farther away, at a distance of about 16,000 light years. It is made up of very old, not young, stars. And, whereas the Pleiades rotates with the other stars in the plane of our Galaxy, Omega Centauri pursues quite a different orbit that takes it above and below the galactic plane.

Omega Centauri is typical of globular clusters. They are all dense globes of very old stars – some appear to be nearly as old as the Galaxy itself. They are all remote, and circle in quite different orbits from ordinary stars within the galactic "halo" – a spherical region of space around the centre of the Galaxy.

A few of the other 150 or so globular clusters are visible to the naked eye. Rivalling Omega Centauri in magnificence in the Southern Hemisphere is 47 Tucanae in Tucana. In the Northern Hemisphere, M13 in Hercules is outstanding, though only just bright enough to be visible to the naked eye. M92, also in Hercules, M3 in Canes Venatici (above) and M15 in Pegasus are somewhat fainter but are excellent subjects for small telescopes.

NEBULAE

The Universe, as we see it, consists of countless galaxies, separated from one another by vast expanses of empty space. In turn, the galaxies consist of billions of stars, separated from one another by apparently empty space.

Space, however, is not completely empty. It contains scattered traces of matter in the form of molecules of gas and particles of dust. In general, this interstellar matter is thinly distributed and difficult to detect, but in places it clumps together into denser clouds, which astronomers call nebulae (after the Latin word for cloud, nebula). Even such "dense" clouds, however, are a million million million times less dense than air!

Bright nebulae

We can see many nebulae in binoculars and telescopes, and a few even with the naked eye, glowing brightly against the dark backdrop of space. The easiest to spot is the Great Nebula in Orion (below), which is visible to skywatchers in both Northern and Southern Hemispheres.

This billowing, flaming cloud is an example of an emission nebula. In this type, gas particles in the cloud give out light when they are excited by (absorb energy from) the radiation from hot stars embedded within them.

Like most emission nebulae, the Orion Nebula is tinged red, and there is a very good reason for this. Red is the colour of the light emitted by hydrogen atoms when they become excited. And hydrogen is the most plentiful element in nebulae.

Other emission nebulae are also spectacular, though most require larger telescopes and long-exposure photography to bring out their true splendour. Many have distinctive shapes that have earned them their names. For example, the Trifid Nebula in Sagittarius has three dark dust lanes running through it; the North America Nebula in Cygnus (right) could not be better named.

When the stars within or near a nebula are cool, their radiation is not energetic enough to excite its atoms. Then the nebula merely reflects the stars' light. Such a reflection nebula is thus relatively faint, and can usually be seen as a diffuse patch of light. The young hot stars in the Pleiades star cluster in Taurus (see page 99) are surrounded by nebulosity of this type.

▼ The Great Nebula (M42) in Orion is perhaps the finest nebula of all, and close enough to be seen with the naked eye. The smaller separate nebula above the Great Nebula is named M43, but it is really an extension of the same nebulosity.

▲ A dramatic close-up of the most famous dark nebula, the aptly named Horsehead Nebula, in Orion. The mass of dark matter is silhouetted against the bright nebula IC434, which extends south from Zeta Orionis, in Orion's Belt.

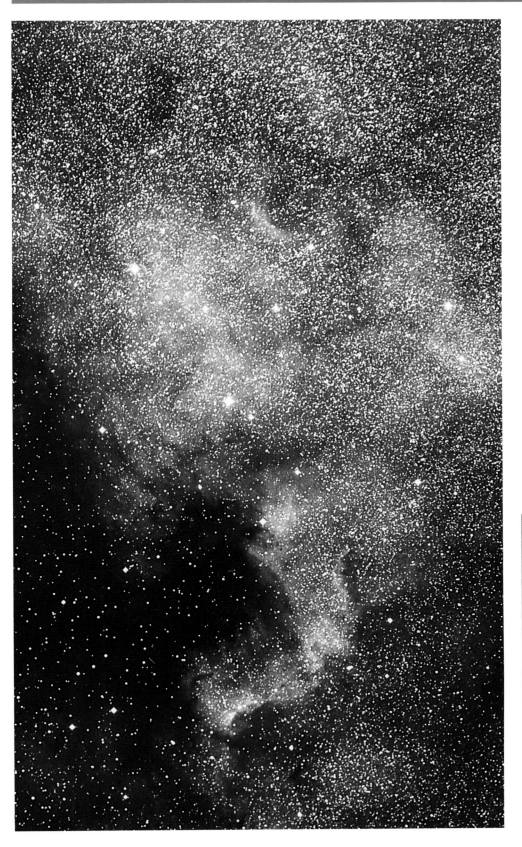

Dark nebulae

There are many clouds of gas and dust in the heavens that are not lit up by nearby or embedded stars. But we can still sometimes detect them, when they blot out the light from more distant stars or nebulae. To our eyes, they appear black, and are termed dark nebulae. Best-known are the Horsehead Nebula in Orion (opposite) and the Coal Sack in Crux.

Astronomers reckon that invisible dark matter makes up quite a large proportion of the mass of the Universe and that the amount of dark matter there is will determine the future of the Universe.

Death throes

Other types of nebulae result when stars approach the end of their lives. A star that has expanded into a red giant often blows off gas, which travels out through space as an expanding spherical shell or bubble. Through a telescope, the gas bubble appears as a diffuse disc, rather like a planet. That is why we call this type a planetary nebula. The Ring Nebula in Lyra (below), the Helix Nebula in Aquarius, and the Dumbbell Nebula in Vulpecula are beautiful examples of the genre.

A writhing cloud of expanding gas also results from the spectacular death of a supergiant star in a supernova (see page 73). The classic example is the Crab Nebula in Taurus (see page 92), the remains of a supernova witnessed by Chinese astronomers in the year 1054. The Veil Nebula in Cygnus (see page 84) is another beautiful example, aptly named after its pattern of glowing filaments, which resemble delicate lacework.

◀ This chaotic area of stars and glowing gas bears an uncanny resemblance to the continent after which it is named, North America. The nebula (NGC7000) is in Cygnus, and can be spotted in binoculars close to Deneb.

▲ The Ring Nebula (M57) in Lyra is a colourful "smoke-ring" of glowing gas and is one of the finest planetary nebulae in the heavens. The ring is made up of gas puffed out by the central star, probably about 6,000 years ago.

THE MILKY WAY

On dark, clear nights, when there is no Moon, you can see a hazy band of light spanning the dome of the heavens. This is aptly named the Milky Way.

The Milky Way passes through some of the most brilliant constellations: Cassiopeia, Cygnus, Perseus, Auriga and Aquila in the Northern Hemisphere, and Puppis, Vela, Carina, Crux, Centaurus, Scorpius and Sagittarius in the Southern Hemisphere. It varies noticeably in brightness. In the Northern Hemisphere, it is brightest in Cygnus and Aquila; in the Southern Hemisphere, in Scorpius and Sagittarius. The Milky Way also varies in width, in places being only about 5° across, while in others approaching 30°.

But what is the Milky Way? No one knew until Galileo turned his telescope on this heavenly band nearly 400 years ago. He was amazed at what he saw, as we are today when we look at it in binoculars. The milky white band resolves into a mass of faint stars beyond number.

In places, for example in Cygnus and Aquila, the Milky Way is split by dark rifts where there appear to be scarcely any stars. The stars are there, but intervening clouds of dust are blotting out their light.

The Milky Way represents a cross-section of the great star system, or galaxy, to which our Sun and all the other stars in the sky belong. We often refer to this system as the Milky Way, but usually we just call it "the Galaxy".

▼ A map of the whole night sky, based on information sent back by the astronomy satellite IRAS, which pictured the Universe in infrared light. It shows, in effect, a cross-section of our Galaxy: the bright region across the middle is the star-studded Milky Way. The large and small white patches underneath are our closest galactic neighbours, the Large and Small Magellanic Clouds.

▲ A view of the Milky Way in the southern constellation Norma, showing dark rifts where dust is obscuring the light from stars behind. This picture, taken in March 1986, shows a celestial interloper, Halley's Comet, which was seen best in the Southern Hemisphere that year.

► Plan and side views of our Galaxy, a typical and quite large spiral. Although most matter is concentrated in the spiral disc, traces exist in a spherical "halo" that surrounds it.

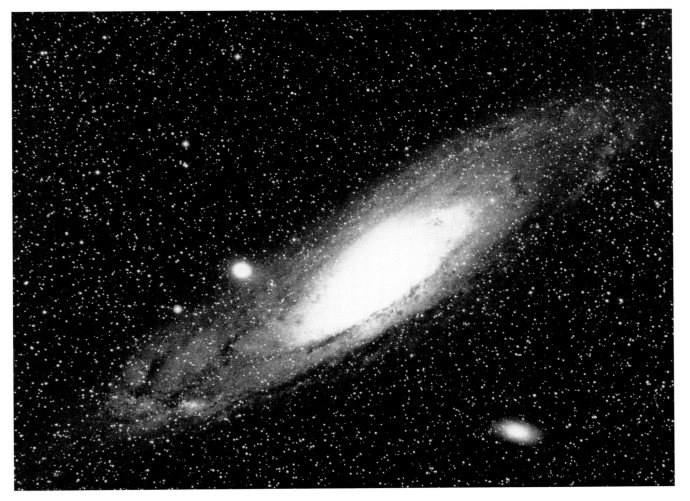

◀ Justly the most famous of all the outer galaxies, the Great Spiral in Andromeda, M31. Visible to the naked eye, its spiral structure mirrors that of our own Galaxy. The Great Spiral has two close companion galaxies, M32 and M110. Both are ellipticals, M32 being the one closest to M31 in the picture.

It takes the form of a disc with a bulge at the centre (the nucleus). From the nucleus a number of arms spiral out, carrying the stars. The whole Galaxy rotates and, viewed from afar, would perhaps present the appearance of a Catherine wheel firework (see left).

The size of our Galaxy is astounding. It measures 100,000 light years across and is made up of at least 100,000 million stars. But it is nothing special among galaxies: it is a typical spiral galaxy of the Sb type (see page 104). Many galaxies, including the Great Spiral in Andromeda (above), are much bigger.

The Sun is located on one of the spiral arms about 30,000 light years from the centre of the Galaxy. Like the other stars, it rotates around the galactic centre, completing one orbit in 225 million years, a period called the cosmic year.

The centre of the Galaxy lies in the direction of Sagittarius, and that is why the Milky Way is densest there and in the neighbouring constellations. We cannot see into the centre because of obscuring dust clouds.

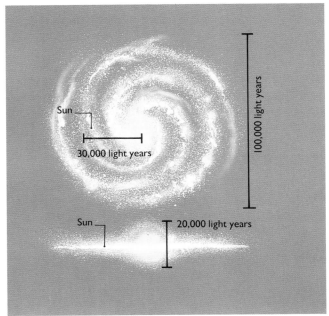

Sun

30,000 light years

100,000 light years

Sun

20,000 light years

▲ Seen edge-on, our own Galaxy would probably look much like this one. It is NGC5907 in Draco, a spiral of the Sb type. Note how the disc thickens towards the centre.

▲ The Large Magellanic Cloud in Dorado, one of the great delights of the Southern Hemisphere. It is visible as a misty patch to the naked eye but easily resolved in telescopes into individual stars. Near the top of this fine photograph is the Tarantula Nebula, one of the largest nebulae we know.

▲ This galaxy is NGC5128 in Centaurus, also called Centaurus A. It is a bright spherical galaxy only just out of naked-eye range. It is notable for the dark dust lane that divides it in two.

▼ Centaurus A in a different light: as it appears at radio wavelengths. It is the third most powerful radio source in the heavens, a sure sign that something devastating is happening inside.

THE OUTER GALAXIES

In the 18th century, the great "collector" of nebulous objects, Charles Messier, listed as number 31 in his catalogue a fuzzy patch visible to the naked eye north of the star Beta Andromedae. It was called the Great Nebula in Andromeda (see page 103).

Only later, when telescopes became more powerful, was it revealed that this "nebula" was actually made up of stars, star clusters and nebulae. It was no nebula of our own Galaxy, but an entirely separate galaxy. When its distance was measured, this was confirmed. The "nebula" lies over two million light years away, very much farther than any of the stars in our Galaxy.

Two other naked-eye "nebulae" also prove to be separate galaxies. They are the Large Magellanic Cloud (LMC) in Dorado and the Small Magellanic Cloud (SMC) in Tucana, which lie close to the southern celestial pole. The LMC, also called Nubecula Major, is in fact the closest galaxy to our own, being only about 170,000 light years away. As far as distances in the Universe are concerned, this is a stone's throw.

Compared with the Great Spiral in Andromeda, the LMC is tiny. The Andromeda Galaxy measures more than 150,000 light years across, half as big again as our own Galaxy and more than five times the size of the LMC.

Classifying the galaxies
The Andromeda Galaxy and the LMC are also poles apart in structure. The one has a fairly regular spiral form,

while the other is quite irregular and shows little structure. These two galaxies typify two major classes of galaxies, the spirals and the irregulars. The third major class of galaxies is elliptical, which covers spherical as well as oval-shaped galaxies.

This classification of galaxies by their shape was suggested by the great pioneer galaxy observer Edwin Hubble in the 1920s. Hubble graded ellipticals E0 to E7 according to how oval they were. He graded spiral galaxies (S) according to the openness of their spiral arms: Sa, Sb and Sc, Sc indicating wide-open arms. Our own Galaxy and Andromeda are both classed as Sb. M33 in Triangulum (page 65) is classed as Sc. Some spiral galaxies have a kind of bar passing through the nucleus, and are classed as barred spirals.

Active galaxies

The majority of galaxies seem to be "normal", giving off the light and energy we would expect for a grouping of billions of stars. But some galaxies have an extraordinary energy output resulting from some extraordinary process going on inside. We call them active galaxies.

Many of the active galaxies send out most of their energy at radio wavelengths. An example is NGC5128, or Centaurus A (left), one of the first radio galaxies to be discovered. Strangely, the energy from a radio galaxy appears to be radiated from a region of space far removed from the galaxy itself!

Clusters of galaxies

Galaxies as well as stars tend to cluster together in space. Our own Galaxy forms part of a cluster called the Local Group. Its 30 or so members also include the Large and Small Magellanic Clouds, the Andromeda Galaxy and M33 in Triangulum.

The Local Group occupies a region of space about 5 million light years across. It is a relatively small cluster. The next cluster to us contains up to 3,000 galaxies! It is the Coma-Virgo Cluster, named after the constellations in which it is found (Coma Berenices and Virgo). It is centred on the bright active galaxy M87.

But the clustering does not stop there. Our Local Group and the Coma-Virgo Cluster are just part of a huge supercluster of galaxies. There are many such superclusters in the Universe.

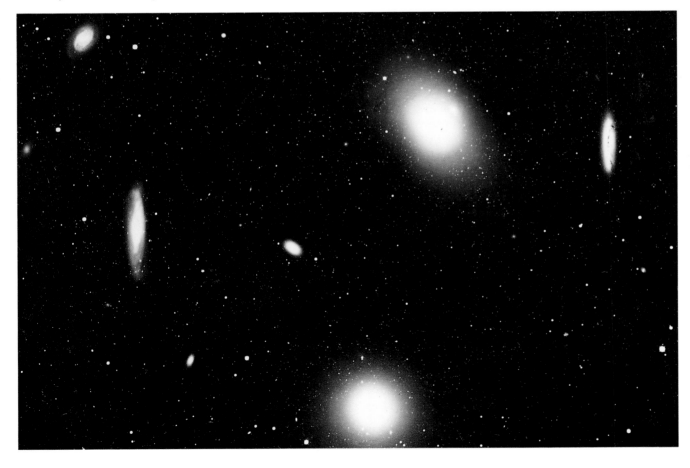

◄ Some of the more prominent members of the Coma-Virgo Cluster, which contains galaxies by the thousand. The largest ones in the picture are a closely matched pair of elliptical galaxies M86 (top) and M84, which are located right at the centre of the Cluster. They are both of the ninth magnitude.

◄ A stunning landscape close to the centre of the Moon, pictured by Apollo astronauts in 1969. The large crater at top right is Ptolemaeus, more than 145 kilometres (90 miles) across. The small crater to its left is Herschel. The similar-sized crater near the bottom of the picture is Lalande.

THE MOON

The distant stars and nebulae and even more remote galaxies are a source of constant delight for the astronomer. But there are plenty of astronomical delights much nearer home. Right on our celestial doorstep is the Moon, the Earth's only natural satellite and by far its closest neighbour in space.

The photograph hints at the pleasures that await us when we turn our binoculars and telescopes on our silvery satellite: craters, flat plains, rugged highlands, wrinkle ridges, and still more craters – always craters.

Being our satellite, the Moon circles around the Earth, taking a little under a month to do so. During this time, it appears to change shape, revealing first more and then less of its surface as it waxes and wanes. The greatest detail can be seen on the terminator, the boundary between light and dark.

The maps in this section show the surface of the Moon in four quadrants. We show it the "right way up", as it appears to the naked eye and through binoculars. Through a telescope, however, these views of the Moon will appear upside-down.

▲ A gibbous Moon, snapped by Apollo astronauts as they sped towards it. The photograph shows well the complex of seas in the eastern hemisphere: Mare Crisium, Serenitatis, Tranquillitatis, Fecunditatis and Nectaris. Use the Moon maps that follow to identify the bright craters.

► The Earth rises above the lunar horizon in one of the classic space photographs taken by the Apollo astronauts. How colourful and inviting the Earth looks compared with the rugged and crater-strewn landscape below.

QUEEN OF THE NIGHT

The Moon is the Earth's constant companion as it journeys through space – its only natural satellite. Although it is relatively small, the Moon dominates the night sky because it is so much closer than any other heavenly body. But the Moon has no light of its own. It shines because it reflects sunlight.

The Moon lies on average about 384,000 kilometres (239,000 miles) away from the Earth, and takes about a month to circle around it. As the Moon circles, we see it go through its phases, with more or less of its surface lit up. The main phases are New Moon, First Quarter, Full Moon and Last Quarter. Between New Moon and First Quarter, and between Last Quarter and New, the Moon appears as a crescent. Between First Quarter and Full, and between Full and Last Quarter, its shape is described as gibbous.

With a diameter of 3,476 kilometres (2,160 miles), the Moon is about a quarter the size of the Earth. This is extraordinarily large for a satellite in relation to its parent planet. So astronomers sometimes consider Earth-Moon as a double planetary system.

Being so small, the Moon has, compared with the Earth, a low mass and therefore weak gravity (one-sixth as strong as the Earth's). As a result, it does not have enough "pull" to hold onto an atmosphere. The airless Moon has no water either. Without an atmosphere, the Moon also experiences a marked difference in temperature between its two-week-long days and nights. In the lunar day temperatures soar to over 100°C (212°F), while in the lunar night they plummet below –150°C (–240°F).

Observing the Moon

Because the Moon appears so large in the night sky, it is the ideal target for the astronomer, and it is popular with newcomer and old-hand alike. The simplest of equipment, binoculars or a small telescope, will reveal a wealth of detail.

Even the naked eye reveals two distinct regions on the Moon – dark and light. The dark ones are the maria, or seas. The light ones are rugged highland areas. Again, the naked eye reveals that the Moon always presents the same face towards us: the nearside. We can never see the farside from Earth. Any optical aid will show the Moon's other major features, its craters and its mountains.

The fascinating thing about lunar observing is that the appearance of the Moon changes nightly as it goes through its phases. In particular, the boundary between light and shadow – lunar day and night – moves over the surface. We call this boundary the terminator. It sweeps over the lunar surface twice – from New to Full, and from Full

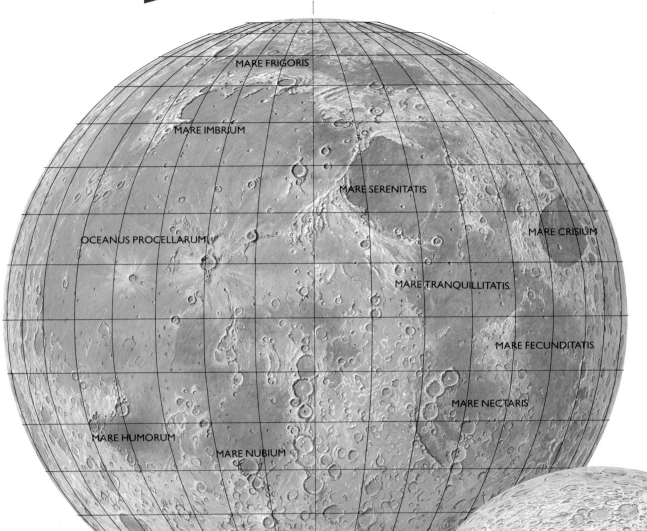

◄ The nearside of the Moon, which always faces us. It is shown the "right-way up", that is, as we see it with the eye and in binoculars. The greater part of the surface is covered with "seas", or maria, which appear darker than the highly cratered highlands. The highlands are thought to be part of the Moon's ancient crust. The maria are younger, formed when gigantic meteorites slammed into the surface and caused the rocks to melt again.

▼ The far side of the Moon, which we can never see from Earth. It remained an enigma until space probes began photographing it, beginning with the Russian Luna 3 probe in 1959. The strange thing about the far side is that it is devoid of any large maria. One of its most recognizable features is a large dark-floored crater named Tsiolkovsky.

back to New, as the Moon waxes and wanes.

It is on the terminator that the greatest detail can be seen. Because of the low Sun angle, long shadows emphasize dramatically the craters, mountains and other surface features. By contrast, Full Moon is not a good time for detailed observation, because the Sun is high up and casts scarcely any defining shadows.

The Moon maps that follow cover the lunar surface in four quadrants. North is at the top. The maps show the most outstanding features of the lunar landscape. The names of the maria and like features are given in Latin. The English equivalents can be found in the Glossary at the end of the book.

NORTH-WEST QUADRANT

Oceanus Procellarum and Mare Imbrium dominate this quadrant. Measuring more than 1,100 kilometres (700 miles) across, Mare Imbrium is the largest of the circular seas. Its boundaries are well defined and marked by high mountain ranges – the Carpathians, Apennines, Caucasus, Alps and Jura Mountains.

The Carpathians, which peak at about 2,100 metres (7,000 feet) extend north-west from Copernicus and form the boundary between Mare Imbrium and Oceanus Procellarum. The Apennines extend for some 450 kilometres (280 miles) and contain some of the highest peaks on the Moon, which soar in places to more than 6,000 metres (20,000 feet). The Caucasus Mountains separate Mare Imbrium from Mare Serenitatis to the east.

Sinus Iridum is a spectacular bay of Mare Imbrium, measuring some 250 kilometres (150 miles) across. It is a spectacular sight on the terminator when the Moon is about 10 days old.

Outstanding craters and other features

Archimedes (75 kilometres, 47 miles) is the largest of a prominent trio of craters, the others being Autolycus and Aristillus. All have flat, lava-filled floors.

Aristarchus is only 37 kilometres (23 miles) across but is the brightest feature on the Moon. Nearby is a deep winding fault called Schroter's Valley.

Copernicus (97 kilometres, 60 miles) is one of the most conspicuous lunar craters. It has a classic profile: high terraced walls and a central mountain peak. At Full Moon it is surrounded by bright crater rays.

Eratosthenes is a two-thirds size replica of Copernicus and lies at the end of the Apennine chain.

Kepler is small (35 kilometres, 22 miles) but stands out prominently on Oceanus Procellarum at Full Moon because of its sparkling crater rays.

Lansberg (42 kilometres, 26 miles), on the lunar equator, stands out clearly on Oceanus Procellarum. It is a near-twin of Reinhold to the north-east.

Otto Struve (160 kilometres, 100 miles) is one of the largest craters in this quadrant, but it is difficult to see because it lies close to the western limb (edge).

Pico is an isolated mountain near the edge of Mare Imbrium, just south of Plato. It rises to about 2,400 metres (8,000 feet).

Plato (97 kilometres, 60 miles), on the edge of the Alps, is a circular crater, noted for its flat and very dark floor.

Reinhold (48 kilometres, 30 miles) lies between Copernicus and Lansberg. Like the latter, it has a deep floor.

Straight Range is an isolated mountain range near the northern edge of Mare Imbrium, close to Plato. It measures about 60 kilometres (40 miles) long and has peaks up to about 1,800 metres (6,000 feet).

▲ Two of the quadrant's most prominent craters, both of which have a characteristic central mountain peak. They are Copernicus (top) and Eratosthenes. The terraced walls of Copernicus are clearly evident.

▶ Another of the quadrant's spectacles, the crater Kepler, as pictured by the Apollo 12 astronauts from lunar orbit. Note how smooth the surrounding mare surface is.

Most of the north-west quadrant is occupied by three seas, the sprawling Oceanus Procellarum, Mare Imbrium and in the north, Mare Frigoris. Oceanus Procellarum is the largest sea on the Moon. Unlike most of the others, it has no definite boundary. Among the craters that grace this quadrant, Copernicus, Kepler and Aristarchus are outstanding, being at the hub of spectacular ray systems at Full Moon.

SOUTH-WEST QUADRANT

Mare Cognitum is often considered to be a bay of Oceanus Procellarum, a sea that altogether covers an area of some 5 million square kilometres (2 million square miles). This is more than half as big again as the Mediterranean Sea on Earth.

Mare Humorum is one of the smaller circular seas, measuring about 450 kilometres (280 miles) across. It is seen best when the Moon is about 11 days old. Mare Nubium is less well defined but boasts a more interesting linear feature called the Straight Wall. Running for about 100 kilometres (60 miles), it marks a fault in the Moon's crust. The Wall is about 240 metres (800 feet) high.

Two of the six Apollo landings were made in this quadrant a few degrees south of the lunar equator:

Apollo 12 set down on Oceanus Procellarum and Apollo 14 near the Fra Mauro formation.

Outstanding craters and other features

Alphonsus (129 kilometres, 80 miles) is the middle one of three large walled plains near the 0° longitude line. Rilles and mountains cross its floor. It is best seen at First Quarter.

Bailly is the largest crater on the Moon, with a diameter of 295 kilometres (183 miles). Unfortunately, it is right on the limb (edge) and is poorly seen at any time.

Bullialdus (50 kilometres, 31 miles), on the edge of Mare Nubium, is a perfectly formed crater with intact walls and central peaks.

Clavius is the largest lunar crater that we can see well from Earth, with a diameter of 232 kilometres (144 miles). Its walls and floor are peppered with craters.

Gassendi (89 kilometres, 55 miles), bordering Mare Humorum, is one of the many fine walled plains this quadrant has to offer. Its floor shows interesting detail.

Grimaldi (193 kilometres, 120 miles) lies a few degrees south of the equator, close to the western limb. It has low walls but it is always easy to spot because of its dark floor. Indeed, it is the darkest area of the Moon.

Longomontanus (145 kilometres, 90 miles) is one of the trio of large craters in the south, the others being Clavius and Maginus. Like them it has partly ruined walls.

Maginus (177 kilometres, 110 miles) lies due east of Longomontanus. These two craters, together with Clavius to the south and Tycho to the north, make a kind of lunar "southern cross".

Pitatus (80 kilometres, 50 miles), at the southern edge of Mare Nubium, has a dark floor with a low central peak.

Ptolemaeus is the first and largest of the string of large craters extending north–south near the 0° longitude line, which are particularly prominent at First Quarter. Close to the Moon's centre, it is a walled plain with a dark floor measuring 148 kilometres (92 miles) across.

Riccioli (160 kilometres, 100 miles) lies just south of the equator near the western limb. Like its neighbour and near-twin Grimaldi, it has an exceptionally dark floor.

Schickard (200 kilometres, 124 miles) is a fine walled plain, with low surrounding walls.

Tycho vies with Copernicus for being the finest lunar crater. Though not big (84 kilometres, 52 miles), it becomes truly spectacular at Full Moon as the centre of a bright crater-ray system, whose shining spokes extend in all directions, as far as Oceanus Procellarum to the north-west and Mare Nectaris to the north-east.

► A close-up picture of the splendid southern crater Tycho, taken by a US Lunar Orbiter probe from a distance of about 220 kilometres (135 miles). Note the crater's terraced walls and the central mountain peak.

▼ At Full Moon Tycho outshines almost every other lunar crater. It is at the hub of the largest crater-ray system on the Moon.

-80° -70° -60° -50° -40° -30° -20° -10° 0°

0°

SINUS MEDII

Lansberg

◇ Apollo 12

◇ Apollo 14

Lalande

Riccioli

Flamsteed

Herschel

Grimaldi

Fra Mauro

Ptolemaeus

OCEANUS PROCELLARUM

-10°

Hansteen

MARE COGNITUM

Alphonsus

Billy

Alperagius

Arzachel

Gassendi

Lubiniezky

MARE NUBIUM

-20°

Bullialdus

Straight Wall

Purbach

MARE HUMORUM

Vieta

Doppelmayer

Pitatus

Regiomontanus

Campanus

-30°

Walter

Lexell

-40°

Hainzel

Wilhelm

Tycho

Schickard

Schiller

Longomontanus

Maginus

-50°

Scheiner

Clavius

Bailly

-60°

-70°

-80°

Oceanus Procellarum spills
into this quadrant, merging
into Mare Cognitum, which
adjoins Mare Nubium and Mare
Humorum. Among the many
craters that dot the quadrant
are a number of huge walled
plains, craters whose floors
have been flooded with lava
relatively recently. None is
finer than Ptolemaeus. The
real showpiece crater,
however, is Tycho, which
becomes dazzlingly prominent
at Full Moon.

N

W   E

S

North-east Quadrant

The circular Mare Serenitatis measures about 700 by 900 kilometres (435 by 560 miles). It is bordered in the north-west by the Caucasus Mountains, which contain peaks of over 6,000 metres (20,000 feet).

The Haemus Mountains to the south are a much lower range. They give way in the east to an area of low hills and small craters, of which the largest is Plinius. The surface of the mare is noticeably wrinkled but features only one prominent crater, Bessel.

▲ A breathtaking view of the south-west region of Mare Tranquillitatis, close to the site of the first Apollo landing on the Moon. The Apollo II lunar module set down near the top centre of the photograph. Maskelyne Rille is in the foreground.

In the north, Mare Serenitatis merges, through Lacus Mortis and Lacus Somniorum, into Mare Frigoris, which extends west into Oceanus Procellarum in the adjacent quadrant. The hilly region in the south of Serenitatis forms an indistinct border between that sea and the similar sized Mare Tranquillitatis. This sea in turn merges into the also irregular Mare Fecunditatis near the equator.

The most distinctly circular sea in this quadrant, however, is Mare Crisium, near the eastern limb. Measuring about 590 by 460 kilometres (370 by 290 miles) across, it is marked by a few small craters, the largest being Picard.

At about the same latitude but on the other side of the quadrant is the small sea Mare Vaporum, which is about 450 kilometres (280 miles) across. It extends south towards the small mare region at the Moon's centre, Sinus Medii.

Three Apollo landings took place in this quadrant: Apollo 11 landed near the south-western edge of Mare Tranquillitatis; Apollo 15 in the Apennines; and Apollo 17 near Littrow crater just beyond the south-eastern edge of Mare Serenitatis.

Outstanding craters and other features

Alpine Valley A valley that cuts through the Alps, in effect linking Mare Imbrium with Mare Frigoris. It looks very much like a river valley on Earth (see page 121), but is actually a particularly straight geological fault.

Aristillus (56 kilometres, 35 miles) is one of a pair (with Autolycus) of small but prominent craters near the eastern edge of Mare Imbrium. It has a deep floor and a central range.

Aristoteles (97 kilometres, 60 miles) is one of another pair (with Eudoxus) of craters north of Mare Serenitatis.

Atlas (89 kilometres, 55 miles) and Hercules form yet another pair of craters in the north of the quadrant.

Autolycus (36 kilometres, 22 miles) forms a conspicuous pair with Aristillus.

Bessel (19 kilometres, 12 miles) is the only notable crater on Mare Serenitatis and therefore easy to spot. It is associated with a crater ray.

Cleomedes (126 kilometres, 78 miles) is a large crater just north of Mare Crisium and looks splendid just after Full Moon, along with the smaller Geminus and Messala farther north.

Eudoxus (64 kilometres, 40 miles) forms a conspicuous pair with Aristoteles.

Gauss (136 kilometres, 85 miles) is one of the largest craters in this quadrant, but is difficult to see because it is right on the limb in the north-east.

Hercules (72 kilometres, 45 miles) forms a pair with Atlas.

Hyginus Rille One of the most prominent rilles on the Moon, running from the south of Mare Vaporum towards Mare Tranquillitatis.

Manilius (36 kilometres, 22 miles), a relatively small crater on the edge of Mare Vaporum, has highly reflective walls, making it one of this quadrant's brightest spots.

Menelaus (32 kilometres, 20 miles) lies on the other side of the Haemus Mountains from Manilius and is also exceptionally bright.

Posidonius (96 kilometres, 60 miles), on the edge of Mare Serenitatis, is a beautiful crater with fascinating walls and well placed for detailed study.

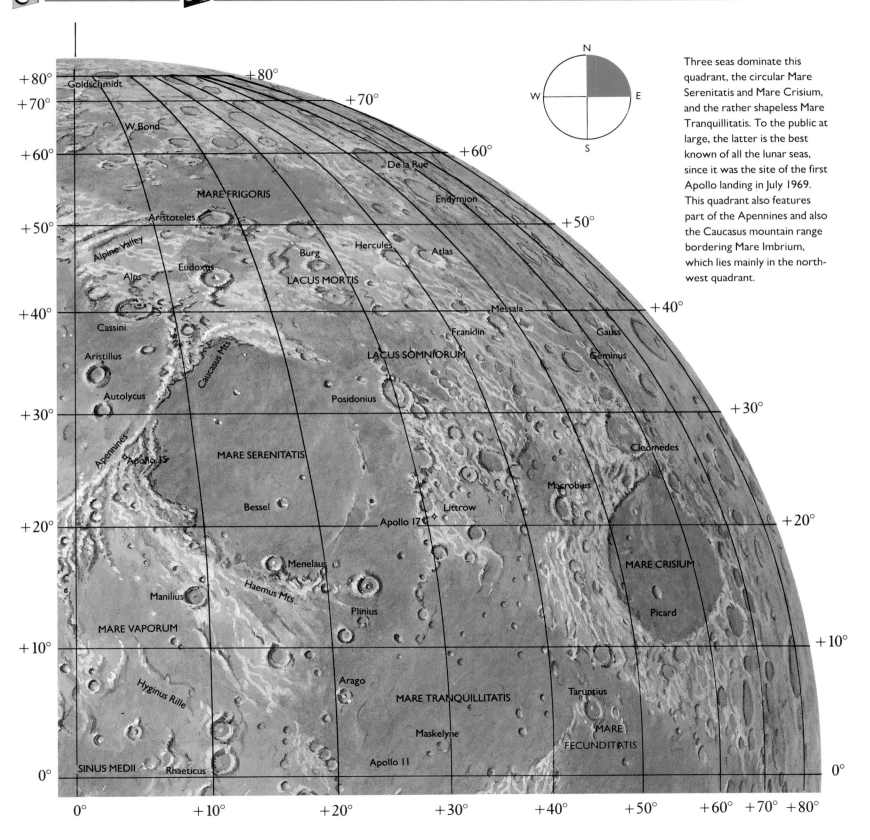

N
W · E
S

Three seas dominate this quadrant, the circular Mare Serenitatis and Mare Crisium, and the rather shapeless Mare Tranquillitatis. To the public at large, the latter is the best known of all the lunar seas, since it was the site of the first Apollo landing in July 1969. This quadrant also features part of the Apennines and also the Caucasus mountain range bordering Mare Imbrium, which lies mainly in the north-west quadrant.

Goldschmidt
W. Bond
De la Rue
Endymion
MARE FRIGORIS
Aristoteles
Alpine Valley
Burg
Hercules
Atlas
Alps
Eudoxus
LACUS MORTIS
Messala
Cassini
Franklin
Gauss
Caucasus Mts
Aristillus
LACUS SOMNIORUM
Geminus
Autolycus
Posidonius
Apennines
Cleomedes
Apollo 15
MARE SERENITATIS
Macrobius
Bessel
Littrow
Apollo 17
Menelaus
MARE CRISIUM
Haemus Mts
Manilius
Plinius
Picard
MARE VAPORUM
Arago
Taruntius
Hyginus Rille
MARE TRANQUILLITATIS
Maskelyne
MARE FECUNDITATIS
SINUS MEDII
Rhaeticus
Apollo 11

+80°   +80°   +70°   +60°   +50°   +40°   +30°   +20°   +10°   0°
+70°
+60°
+50°
+40°
+30°
+20°
+10°
0°

0°   +10°   +20°   +30°   +40°   +50°   +60°   +70°   +80°

SOUTH-EAST QUADRANT

The irregularly shaped Mare Fecunditatis is flanked in the east by a chain of large craters, including Langrenus, Vendelinus and Petavius.

Beyond this sea, right on the limb and straddling the equator is Mare Smythii, which can be seen best at or shortly after Full Moon. Mare Australe, which is on the limb in the far south, can also be glimpsed at this time.

Mare Nectaris is well defined and is surrounded by a ring of large craters, including Theophilus, Catharina and Fracastorius. Beyond this arc of craters lies the only prominent mountain range in this quadrant, the Altai Mountains, or Scarp. They run for about 500 kilometres (300 miles) from near Catharina to Piccolomini and reach a height of about 4,000 metres (13,000 feet). The range was probably formed by the same impact that created Mare Nectaris.

Outstanding craters and other features

Albategnius (129 kilometres, 80 miles) is an ancient walled plain south of Hipparchus. It shows up well at First Quarter, when it is on the terminator. It has a central range, and in the south-west has a deep crater, Klein, embedded in its walls.

Aliacensis (84 kilometres, 52 miles) is the largest of a chain of craters in the west. It forms a distinct pair with its neighbour, the slightly smaller Werner.

Fabricus (89 kilometres, 55 miles) spoils the large ruined plain Janssen and adjoins the similar-sized crater Metius.

Fracastorius (97 kilometres, 60 miles) is a badly ruined crater almost obliterated during the formation of Mare Nectaris, of which it now forms a bay.

Hipparchus (145 kilometres, 90 miles) is an ancient walled plain close to the Moon's centre. It forms a pair with Albategnius but it is more ruined. It has low walls and is not easy to spot except when on the terminator.

Langrenus (137 kilometres, 85 miles) is the most prominent of the chain of large craters that more or less follow the 60° longitude line in the east.

Maurolycus (109 kilometres, 68 miles) is an example of an ancient crater, badly eroded by later impacts.

Petavius (170 kilometres, 106 miles) One of the "big three" craters (with Langrenus and Vendelinus) on the 60° longitude line in the east. It is magnificent around Full Moon, sending out bright rays that meet those coming from Tycho in the adjacent quadrant.

Piccolomini (80 kilometres, 50 miles) lies at the southern end of the Altai range. It stands out because there are no large craters nearby.

Rheita (68 kilometres, 42 miles) is close to one of the finest crater chains on the Moon, the 160-kilometre (100-mile) long Rheita Valley.

Theophilus (100 kilometres, 62 miles) is the largest of the arc of craters west of Mare Nectaris. It has well-terraced walls and a deep floor with a central range.

Vendelinus (165 kilometres, 103 miles) lies between Langrenus and Petavius in the string of large craters in the east. It is undoubtedly more ancient than the others and has low walls. It is much less prominent than the other two.

Walter (129 kilometres, 80 miles) lies right on the 0° longitude line and is the southernmost of a string of large craters that lies just in the south-east quadrant (Ptolemaeus, Alphonsus, Arzachel, Purbach, Regiomontanus).

▼ This was part of the haul of Moon rocks brought back to Earth by the Apollo 16 astronauts. It is a typical volcanic rock containing many vesicles, or cavities, made by gas escaping when the molten rock cooled and set.

► Langrenus is perhaps the finest crater in this quadrant. It has high terraced walls, a central mountain range, and is spectacularly bright almost all the time.

SINUS MEDII   MARE TRANQUILLITATIS

MARE SMYTH.II

Hipparchus

MARE FECUNDITATIS

Ptolemaeus   Apollo 16

Gutenberg   Langrenus

Albategnius

Goclenius

Abulfed

Cyrillus   Theophilus

Colombo

MARE NECTARIS

Arzachel

Vendelinus

Catharina

Altai Mens

Fracastorius

Petavius

Purbach   Apianus

Regiomontanus

Werner

Piccolomini

Sheilius

Aliacensis

Stevinus

Walter

Rheita

Furnerius

Maurolycus

Rheita Valley

Stöfler

Metius

Fabricus

Pitiscus

Vlacq

MARE AUSTRALE

Manzinus

Curtius

This quadrant contains a relatively small area of seas. Mare Tranquillitatis extends into it from the north, as does Mare Fecunditatis. The only sea wholly in this quadrant is the small Mare Nectaris. The terrain consists mainly of rugged highlands, but high mountain ranges are noticeably absent. There are more craters here than in any of the other quadrants, with a spectacular chain of large craters in the east.

Phases of the Moon

As the Moon circles around the Earth every month, we see it go through its phases (*above*). The phases come about because, viewed from the Earth, sunlight lights up more or less of the Moon's face as it travels in its orbit.

The diagram (*left*) helps explain this. It shows the kind of view we would see if we could look down on the Earth-Moon system from above the North Pole. The numbers relate the positions of the Moon in its orbit at various times to the equivalent phase we view from Earth.

The diagrams above show how the phases come about. At New Moon phase, the Sun, the Moon and the Earth are more or less lined up in space. The Sun lies on the opposite side of the Moon and lights up the farside. But the nearside is not lit up, so we cannot see it. After a few days the Moon has moved far enough out of alignment for the Sun to light up a little of the nearside; then we see the Moon as a crescent.

The process continues, with more and more of the nearside being lit up, until the Moon is again lined up with the Sun and the Earth, but opposite the Sun in the sky. The whole nearside is now lit up, and we have a Full Moon. The reverse process then takes place, with less and less of the nearside illuminated, until at the next New Moon we again cannot see the nearside.

Occasionally – as the Moon orbits the Earth and the Earth orbits the Sun – Sun, Moon and Earth come into exact or almost exact alignment. Then eclipses occur. An eclipse of the Sun occurs when, at New Moon phase, the Moon's disc covers the Sun's and blots out its light (see page 128). An eclipse of the Moon occurs when at Full Moon phase, the Moon moves into the Earth's shadow.

MOON MOVEMENTS

▶ A waxing gibbous Moon, 10 days old. Note the interesting detail in the Mare Imbrium region: Sinus Iridium is nicely outlined, and the flat floor of Plato is distinctly dark. Nearby, Alpine Valley can be seen cutting through the mountains. Copernicus and its ray system are also clearly seen here.

▶ (*Opposite*) A magnificent photograph of the Moon in eclipse. The surface is lit up with a reddish hue by sunlight that has been refracted by the Earth's atmosphere, which acts like a lens. Note that we can still clearly see Tycho and some of its rays.

As regularly as clockwork, every 29½ days, the Moon goes through its phases. This time period is one of the great natural divisions of time, on which we base our calendar month (= one "moonth").

Like most other heavenly bodies, the Moon has two movements in space: it spins on its axis, it travels in orbit around the Earth. The Moon spins round once on its axis every 27⅓ days. It also takes exactly the same period of time to travel once in orbit around the Earth. The consequence of this is that the Moon always presents the same face – the nearside – towards us. We say it has a "captured rotation".

The Moon's movement in orbit gives rise to its changing appearance in the sky, which we describe as its phases. It takes about two days longer for the Moon to go through its phases than to orbit the Earth. This happens because the Earth itself is moving in its orbit around the Sun.

▲ A classic lunar crater, IAU 308, located on the farside of the Moon. It has terraced walls, a central mountain range and measures about 80 kilometres (50 miles) across.

▲ The smooth surface of Mare Tranquillitatis is typical of the extensive maria on the lunar nearside. Craters are few and generally small.

▼ By contrast, the surface of the lunar farside is rugged and heavily cratered. At bottom left is a small sea area, Mare Moscoviense.

THE LUNAR SURFACE

The surface of the Moon is fascinating at whatever distance we view it. The two major types of lunar landscape are the maria and the terrae – the seas and the highlands.

Both types of landscape bear witness to the bombardment the Moon has suffered from outer space in the craters that scar their surface. The floors of the maria and many of the large craters are marked by many other geological features, including rilles, ridges, faults and domes.

The maria
On the nearside of the Moon the landscape is dominated by maria; in contrast, the farside has no maria of appreciable size. The maria have many fewer craters than the terrae, indicating that they are more recent in origin. The terrae are thought to be part of the Moon's original crust.

Analyses of rock samples brought back by the Apollo

▼ This intriguing crater chain runs in a south-westerly direction from a small crater on the edge of Ptolemaeus towards the crater Davy.

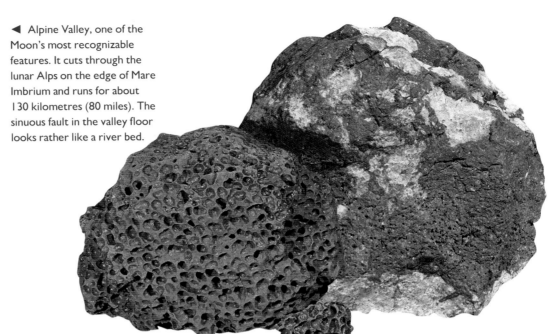

◄ Alpine Valley, one of the Moon's most recognizable features. It cuts through the lunar Alps on the edge of Mare Imbrium and runs for about 130 kilometres (80 miles). The sinuous fault in the valley floor looks rather like a river bed.

astronauts indicate that the maria may be as young as 3.2 billion years old, while the highlands may be up to 1 billion years older.

The maria formed when massive meteorites or asteroids crashed into the Moon and gouged out huge basins. The basins were subsequently filled by vast outpourings of molten lava. On average the maria are several kilometres lower than the mean sphere of the Moon.

The craters

The craters that pepper the lunar surface were in the main also created by the impact of meteorites. The classic lunar crater has walls that rise above the surrounding surface and a floor that is lower.

One of the deepest lunar craters is the 113-kilometre (70-mile) diameter Newton, close to the south pole. The walls rise over 2 kilometres (1.2 miles) above the surrounding landscape and plunge nearly 9 kilometres (5.6 miles) below it.

When craters form, huge amounts of material are ejected from them. This "ejecta" is clearly visible around many of the younger lunar craters, such as Copernicus and Tycho. It shines brightly as crater rays, which are spectacular at Full Moon.

Material ejected from a large crater can also create lines of small craters, known as crater chains. But other kinds of crater chains may be the result of volcanic activity along a fault line in the crust.

Some of the larger craters, such as Plato and Grimaldi, are notable for their low walls and smooth, flat floor. They are rather like miniature maria, and are examples of what are termed walled plains.

Rilles and ridges

Volcanic activity in the crust has also created a number of other linear features. The most prominent are the rilles, also called rimae. They are trench-like features, which can be up to about 5 kilometres (3 miles) wide and a few hundred metres deep. The winding, or sinuous rilles are thought to be ancient lava channels, or mark where subsurface lava tubes have collapsed. Straight rilles probably resulted when blocks of rock slipped downwards along fault lines.

One of the most conspicuous rilles is Hyginus Rille between Mare Vaporum and Mare Tranquillitatis. Hadley Rille, in the Apennines, was visited by Apollo 15 astronauts.

Just as there are sinuous depressions – rilles – so there are sinuous elevations. Called "wrinkle ridges", they snake across most of the maria. Some seem to be associated with volcanic activity; others seem to have formed when the maria surface cooled.

▲ Breccia, one of the two main kinds of Moon rock, made up of pieces of old rocks cemented together.

▲ (left) Basalt, the other main kind of Moon rock. This sample is riddled with cavities where gas escaped when the molten rock cooled.

▲ The intriguing orange soil, discovered in Taurus-Littrow Valley by the Apollo 17 astronauts.

THE APOLLO EXPLORATIONS

It was late evening on July 20 1969, at the Kennedy Space Center in Florida, and early morning on July 21 in Europe, when a most momentous event took place 385,000 kilometres (240,000 miles) away.

Neil Armstrong, a being from planet Earth, stepped down onto the Moon's surface. "That's one small step for a man, one giant leap for mankind," he said.

Armstrong was the first of a dozen US astronauts who, over the next three-and-a-half years, took part in the most exciting exploration project humans have ever attempted. The project was called Apollo. It had begun in earnest following President John F. Kennedy's plea to the American people in 1961 to land a man on the Moon "before the decade is out". NASA, the National Aeronautics and Space Administration, achieved this goal for them with six months of the decade left.

The Apollo hardware

The technique chosen to land astronauts on the Moon called for a crew of three, a three-part spacecraft weighing some 45 tonnes (50 tons), and a gigantic rocket, the 111-metre (365-foot) tall Saturn V, to launch it.

The technique chosen to effect a Moon landing – lunar orbit rendezvous – involved separation and rendezvous manoeuvres in lunar orbit. It required two of the crew to descend to the surface in a landing vehicle, the lunar

module, while the third crew member continued to circle overhead in the mother ship, the CSM (command and service modules). After the surface exploration, the moonwalkers returned in the top part of the lunar module and rendezvoused with the CSM, in which they all returned to Earth.

The first historic Moon landing, by Apollo 11, took

▶ The Apollo 11 lunar module ascends into orbit to rendezvous with the CSM after the first successful lunar landing. The mare below is Mare Smythii. In the Moon sky, Planet Earth is at quarter phase.

▼ The Apollo 11 CSM in orbit, pictured from the lunar module. The landscape below is located in the north central region of Mare Fecunditatis. The perfect symmetry of the crater at top left shows that it is relatively new.

▶ The most famous picture of the Space Age: second man-on-the-Moon Edwin Aldrin posing for a picture during the first Moon-landing mission. First man-on-the-Moon Neil Armstrong, the photographer, is reflected in Aldrin's visor. So is the Apollo 11 lunar module.

place on Mare Tranquillitatis. Armstrong and fellow moonwalker Edwin Aldrin trod the lunar soil for two-and-a-half hours, collected over 21 kilograms (46 pounds) of rock samples, and a collection of stunning photographs.

Apollo 12 (November 1969) landed on the edge of Oceanus Procellarum. During the mission the first of five automatic scientific stations known as ALSEP (Apollo lunar surface experiments package) was set up. The Apollo 13 mission (April 1970) had to be aborted when an explosion disabled the spacecraft en route to the Moon. Apollo 14 (February 1971) set down in the region of Fra Mauro.

The remaining three missions took place in much more dramatic landscapes: Apollo 15 (July 1971) in the foothills of the Apennines, Apollo 16 (April 1972) in the highlands near Descartes crater, and Apollo 17 (December 1972) in the Taurus-Littrow Valley near the edge of Mare Serenitatis. On all three missions, the moonwalkers were much more mobile than their earlier colleagues, for they had transport, in the form of the lunar rover.

In all, the Apollo astronauts spent nearly 170 hours exploring the lunar surface. They travelled almost 100 kilometres (62 miles) in the lunar rover. They collected 385 kilograms (850 pounds) of rock and soil samples, and 50 core samples. They took 30,000 photographs on the surface and from lunar orbit, and acquired all kinds of data on 20,000 reels of magnetic tape.

Scientifically and technologically, Apollo was an outstanding triumph. Posterity will have to judge whether it was worth the 25 billion dollars it cost.

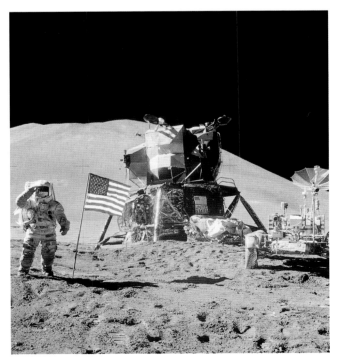

▲ Geologist Harrison Schmitt works near a huge split boulder at Taurus-Littrow on the Apollo 17 mission (the last).

► Mount Hadley provides the backdrop as James Irwin salutes the "Stars and Stripes" at the start of the Apollo 15 mission to the foothills of the Apennines. At right is the lunar rover, being used on the Moon for the first time.

◄ Edwin Aldrin struggling with a core-sampling drill on the flat landscape of Mare Tranquillitatis during the historic first Moon landing. The core samples give clues to the history of the lunar surface.

◀ This false-colour picture shows the Sun's corona, its outer atmosphere of rarified gases that extends for millions of kilometres in all directions before it merges imperceptibly into interplanetary space. This was one of the incomparable pictures taken in 1973 during the Skylab project.

THE SUN

Asked the question "Which is the nearest star?", we would probably reply Proxima Centauri, a faint red dwarf more than 4 light years away. But strictly speaking this is wrong. The nearest star to us is a quite bright yellow dwarf, only 8.5 light minutes away – the daytime star we call the Sun.

This golden orb, which arcs through our skies by day, pours out the light and heat that makes life on Earth possible in its myriad of different forms. Astronomers study the Sun closely, since its behaviour mirrors that of the majority of the stars in the Universe.

But the amateur astronomer must study the Sun with care, since its blinding light will indeed blind. It must never be observed directly through binoculars or telescopes. However, these instruments can be used to project solar images, which will reveal such phenomena as sunspots and eclipses.

Total eclipses of the Sun are phenomena that many astronomers rave over and journey to the ends of the Earth to see. And for good reason. They are among the most beautiful, the most exciting, and the most awesome happenings in nature.

▲ The golden orb of the Sun, about to sink below the horizon at Cape Canaveral in Florida. At sunset the sky turns reddish orange because dust in the lower layers of the atmosphere blocks the shorter wavelengths in sunlight.

▼ Impromptu solar astronomy in the Australian outback in March 1986, when Halley's Comet chasers pause to witness a partial solar eclipse. A double image of the partially eclipsed Sun is obtained by projection through binoculars.

▲ A huge tongue of incandescent gas shoots out from the Sun's surface more than 500,000 kilometres (300,000 miles). It is one of the spectacular solar prominences witnessed in 1973 during the Skylab mission.

DAYTIME STAR

Our daytime star, the Sun, is a huge globe of hot gas, about 1,390,000 kilometres (865,000 miles) in diameter. It is a very average star, much bigger than some, but much smaller than others.

The Sun is 750 times more massive than all the other bodies in the Solar System put together. With such a huge mass, it has very powerful gravity, which keeps these bodies captive.

The Sun lies at an average distance from Earth of about 150 million kilometres (93 million miles). We call this distance one astronomical unit (AU).

The Sun pours out into space a fantastic amount of energy, not only as light and heat (infra-red rays), but also as many other kinds of radiation, such as gamma rays, X-rays, ultraviolet rays and radio waves. It has poured out this energy since it was born, some 4,600 million years ago. And it should continue to do so for another 5,000 million years. This energy is produced by nuclear fusion reactions taking place in the hydrogen gas in the Sun's core.

Solar energy radiates away from the visible surface of the Sun, which we call the photosphere ("light-sphere").

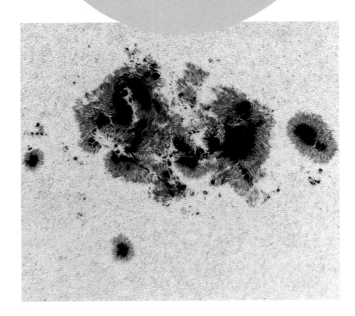

or so. And they come and go according to a "sunspot cycle" of about 11 years. We can study sunspots using a telescope to project an image of the Sun onto a white card. **Never look directly at the Sun through a telescope or binoculars**.

Often associated with sunspots are eruptions called flares. They give rise to streams of charged particles, which greatly increase the solar wind, the normal outflow of particles from the Sun.

It is at such times, when the solar wind "blows" exceptionally strongly, that magnetic storms and aurorae occur on Earth. Aurorae are visible mainly in far northern and far southern skies, where they are known respectively as the aurora borealis ("Northern Lights") and aurora australis ("Southern Lights"). They take the form of lovely glows and shimmering curtains of coloured light. The light is given off when the charged particles of the solar wind collide with air particles high in the atmosphere.

◀ A well-developed sunspot group. Note in each spot the dark umbra at the centre and the surrounding lighter penumbra. Some sunspots can grow to more than 200,000 kilometres (125,000 miles) across and persist for months.

◀ (*Top*) Sunspots are the visible signs of violent activity taking place on the Sun's surface.

▼ The aurora borealis, viewed from Kitt Peak National Observatory, Arizona, in April 1981. It is unusual for vivid aurorae to occur at such low latitudes, and indicates that violent activity was taking place on the Sun at the time.

Its temperature is about 6,000°C (11,000°F). Above the photosphere is the Sun's lower atmosphere, called the chromosphere ("colour-sphere") because of its reddish colour. And above that is the outer atmosphere, the corona, which becomes increasingly more rarified until it merges into the near-vacuum of space. Because the photosphere is so bright, we can see the chromosphere and corona only during a total eclipse of the Sun.

The Sun's surface is in constant turmoil as hot gases well up from below. Sometimes great fountains of flaming gas called prominences shoot high above the surface. From time to time, dark regions develop and grow. We call these regions sunspots. They appear to move across the solar disc as the Sun rotates on its axis once every 25 days

▼ A total solar eclipse occurs when the Moon's shadow falls on the Earth.

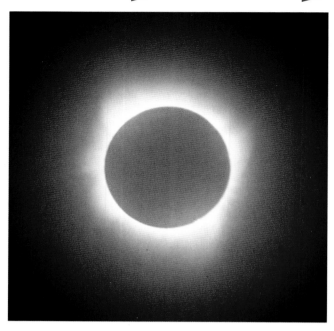

▲ The author's record of the March 18, 1988, total eclipse, viewed from Bangka Island, Indonesia. (*Left*) Seconds before totality, the Moon's shadow is clearly visible. (*Right*) During totality the corona is brilliant.

▼ The author, appropriately attired for viewing the long total eclipse from Hawaii (July 11, 1991)! Note the simplicity of the equipment: ordinary camera with telephoto lens and mylar filter, cable shutter release, tripod.

OBSERVING SOLAR ECLIPSES

Sun

Moon

Umbra

Penumbra

Earth

Of all the natural phenomena we witness on Earth none is more spectacular or more awe-inspiring than a total eclipse of the Sun. During an eclipse, day turns suddenly into night; the air chills; birds stop singing and start to roost.

Eclipses of the Sun occur because of a strange astronomical coincidence. The Sun is four hundred times farther away from the Earth than the Moon, but its diameter is four hundred times greater than that of the Moon. The consequence of this is that both Sun and Moon appear much the same size in the Earth sky.

From time to time as the Moon travels in orbit around the Earth it lines up exactly with the Sun and the Earth. When it comes between them, it blots out the Sun's light and casts a shadow on the Earth and we have an eclipse of the Sun, or a solar eclipse. When the Moon is on the other side of the Earth from the Sun, it enters the shadow cast by the Earth and we have an eclipse of the Moon, or a lunar eclipse (see pages 118 and 119).

On average, solar eclipses occur about twice a year but they are not always total; they are often partial, the Moon covering only part of the Sun's disc. Sometimes they are annular, the Moon covering up all of the Sun's disc except for an annulus, or ring, around the edge.

Even under the most favourable conditions during a total eclipse, the diameter of the umbra, or complete shadow, cast on the Earth by the Moon is seldom more than about 270 kilometres (170 miles). This shadow sweeps out a "path of totality" as it races across the Earth at speeds of several thousand kilometres an hour. The maximum duration of totality occurs in the middle of the path, along the centre line. The longest any total eclipse can occur is theoretically about seven-and-a-half minutes. But over the next 50 years it is predicted that the longest (in July 2009) will be 6 minutes 38 seconds. Most will be much shorter.

Here is a brief summary of total eclipse "events". The Moon takes on average about two hours to pass across the Sun. The partial phase of the eclipse begins at "first contact", as the Moon takes its first "bite" out of the Sun's disc. About an hour later, with the light fading perceptibly all the while, comes "second contact", the beginning of totality. Just before this comes the phenomenon of "Baily's Beads", as beads of sunlight shine through the valleys on the limb of the Moon.

During totality, vivid pink prominences show up around the dark disc of the Moon. Then the Sun's pearly white corona appears. More Baily's Beads precede the end of totality ("third contact"). Then the Sun emerges once more, creating for an instant a beautiful "diamond ring". About an hour later the Moon completely clears the Sun ("fourth contact") and the eclipse is over.

For the total eclipse of July 11, 1991, eclipse-watchers – the author among them – descended on the Big Island of Hawaii in their thousands. At about 7.28 in the morning, the Sun went into total eclipse for the relatively long period of 4 minutes 12 seconds. The author witnessed the event from Kailua Kona, close to the centre line of the path of totality. Clouds threatened to mar the occasion, but fortuitously rolled away minutes before totality. Thousands of others on the island were not so lucky.

▼ During totality, the sky is not completely dark. It is tinged orange on the horizon.

▶ The Moon has already taken a significant "bite" out of the Sun. Cloud is creating a halo.

▼ Eclipse is total. Vivid prominences leap into view at 12 o'clock and 6 o'clock.

▲ An exquisite "diamond ring" signals the end of totality; daylight is about to return.

◄ The ringed planet Saturn, pictured here with six of its moons against a stellar background. It is a montage of photographs taken by the Voyager I space probe. The moon in the foreground is Dione; then, going clockwise, come Enceladus, Rhea, Titan, Mimas and Tethys.

6

THE SUN'S FAMILY

The Sun is really massive and consequently has an enormous gravitational pull, which reaches out thousands of millions of kilometres into space. It holds together a varied collection of heavenly bodies, large and small. They form the Sun's family, or Solar System.

The Earth is one of the larger bodies in the Solar System that we call planets. There are eight more planets, four smaller than the Earth and four very much larger. Three of the other planets in particular – Venus, Mars and Jupiter – far outshine the brightest stars and are easy to follow as they wander across the celestial sphere month by month in and out of the constellations.

As well as planets, the Sun's family includes more than 60 moons, thousands of mini-planets, or asteroids, and unknown numbers of icy lumps, which become visible as comets when they approach the Sun. Even specks of interplanetary dust reveal their presence in the night sky when they burn up in the atmosphere, creating meteors or shooting stars. All these bodies make rewarding study, with the naked eye as well as with binoculars and telescopes.

THE SOLAR SYSTEM

Until the sixteenth century, people believed that the Earth was fixed at the centre of the Universe, and that all the heavenly bodies circled around it. This followed the system laid down by the Greek astronomer Ptolemy in about AD 150.

▼ The planets are the major bodies in the Solar System. They circle around it at different distances, but in much the same plane. Viewed from the "north", the planets travel anticlockwise around the Sun. All except Venus also spin on their own axis anticlockwise. In this diagram the orbits of the planets are drawn roughly to scale.

Some astronomers were dissatisfied with this belief, which could not readily account for the observed motions of the planets.One was Copernicus, who realized that planetary motions could be explained if the Sun and not the Earth were at the centre of the Universe. Because he relegated the Earth to the status of a mere planet, the Church regarded Copernicus's views as heresy. They were not generally accepted until early the next century, when Kepler worked out his celebrated laws of planetary motion.

Copernicus had no idea of the scale of the Solar System, nor had any astronomers until comparatively recent times. We know now that it reaches out from the Sun far beyond the Earth and indeed far beyond the orbit of Pluto, usually the most distant planet we know.

Pluto wanders at times over 7 billion kilometres (4.5 billion miles) from the Sun. But way beyond the path of that maverick planet lurks a "belt" of icy lumps (the Kuiper Belt) and beyond that a similarly composed "cloud" (the Oort Cloud). This "cloud" is thought to be a reservoir of icy bodies that occasionally stray into the inner Solar System and become visible as comets. It is thought that the Oort Cloud could reach out more than two light years from the Sun – half-way to the nearest stars. The existence of such far-distant bodies seems to have been confirmed by the discovery in 1992 of an object (QB1) beyond Pluto's orbit. Some 200 kilometres (125 miles) across, it could be part of the Kuiper Belt.

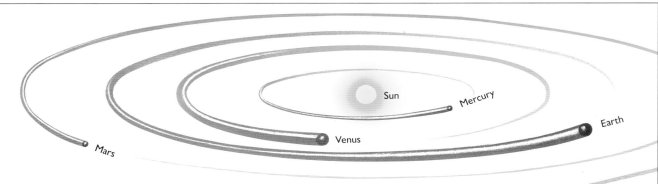

◄ This inset diagram shows the orbits of the four inner planets to scale. Mercury, Venus and Mars are called the terrestrial planets because they are rocky bodies like the Earth.

Planet		Mercury	Venus	Earth	Mars	Jupiter	Saturn	Uranus	Neptune	Pluto
Diameter at equator	(km)	4,878	12,104	12,756	6,794	142,800	120,000	51,200	49,500	2,280
	(miles)	3,031	7,521	7,926	4,222	88,700	74,600	31,800	30,800	1,430
Mean distance from Sun (×10⁶)	(km)	60	108	150	228	778	1,430	2,870	4,500	5,900
	(miles)	37.5	67.5	93.5	143	486	890	1,790	2,810	3,690
Circles Sun in		88 days	225 days	365.25 days	687 days	11.9 years	29.5 years	84 years	165 years	248 years
Spins on axis in		58.6 days	243 days	23.93 hours	24.6 hours	9.8 hours	10.2 hours	16.3 hours	16 hours	6.3 days
Mass (Earth = 1)		0.06	0.82	1.00	0.11	318	95	14.5	17.2	0.002
Volume (Earth = 1)		0.05	0.88	1.00	0.15	1,316	755	52	44	0.005
Density (water = 1)		5.4	5.2	5.5	3.9	1.3	0.7	1.3	1.8	2
Number of moons		0	0	1	2	16+	22+	15+	8+	1

▼ Pluto's orbit takes it a long way above and below the other planets. The orbit is highly eccentric, and takes Pluto at times inside the orbit of Neptune. It is inside Neptune's orbit at present, and will remain there until 1999. Then it will resume its rightful place as the most distant planet.

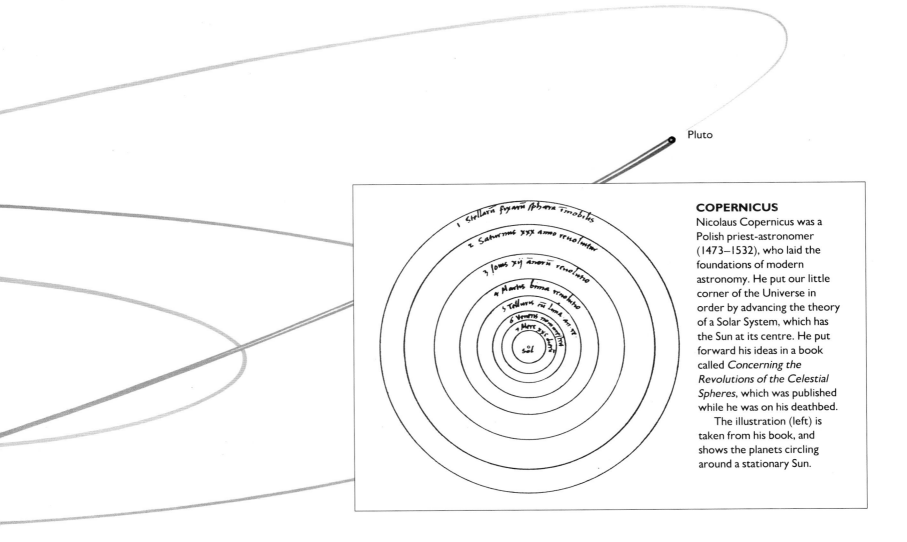

Pluto

COPERNICUS
Nicolaus Copernicus was a Polish priest-astronomer (1473–1532), who laid the foundations of modern astronomy. He put our little corner of the Universe in order by advancing the theory of a Solar System, which has the Sun at its centre. He put forward his ideas in a book called *Concerning the Revolutions of the Celestial Spheres*, which was published while he was on his deathbed.

The illustration (left) is taken from his book, and shows the planets circling around a stationary Sun.

▲ Three views of Mars during the opposition of 1967. Note the north polar ice cap, the whitish haze in places, and various dark markings.

▼ (*Right*) Saturn through a telescope. The "A" and "B" rings stand out clearly.

(*Middle*) Jupiter through a telescope, showing prominent belts and zones and a vivid Great Red Spot.

(*Left*) Jupiter shining brightly alongside a cloud-shrouded Full Moon.

OBSERVING PLANETS AND ASTEROIDS

Five planets – Mercury, Venus, Mars, Jupiter and Saturn – were known to the ancients, for they can be seen with the naked eye. When most favourably placed for observation, they rival or outshine even the brightest stars. They show up in telescopes as distinct discs rather than points.

From the amateur's point of view these five planets most reward observation. The others – Uranus, Neptune and Pluto – are too remote to show anything of interest.

Because of their brilliance, Venus, Jupiter and often Mars are easy to spot in the night sky. Mercury and Saturn are rather more elusive. You can find out exactly where the planets are at any time by consulting astronomical magazines and yearbooks.

The motion of the planets through the heavens is not entirely straightforward. For example, Mars, Jupiter and Saturn, which normally travel eastwards against the background of stars, sometimes start travelling westwards, or in a retrograde direction. This happens because the Earth, travelling more quickly inside their orbit, periodically catches up with and then overtakes them. And they appear to "loop the loop" in the sky.

Mercury and Venus

Although Mercury is not very far away, it is not easy to pick up. This is because it orbits relatively close to the Sun, and therefore stays near it in the sky. At its most favourable, Mercury can reach magnitude –1.9. Venus is very much easier to see. It is much nearer than Mercury and much bigger, and at maximum brightness reaches a magnitude of –4.4.

When either of these planets lies east of the Sun, they are visible in the west after sunset. When they lie west of the Sun, they are visible in the east before sunrise. In other words, they are either evening or morning stars.

Mars

This planet, when most favourably placed, reaches a magnitude of –2.8, outshining all the other planets except Venus. It can readily be distinguished from the others because of its orange-red colour, which earns it the name of the Red Planet.

Whereas little detail can be seen on the disc of Venus and Mercury, Mars is more revealing. It shows prominent ice caps at the poles and dark markings that come and go with the changing seasons.

Asteroids, or minor planets

These mini-planets orbit in a broad "belt" between the orbits of Mars and Jupiter. The largest ones – the biggest is Ceres, about 1,000 kilometres (620 miles) across – can be glimpsed and photographed moving against the background of stars (*see below*).

Jupiter and Saturn

Jupiter is by far the largest planet and it is covered with clouds that reflect sunlight well. This adds up to it rivalling Mars in brightness, reaching up to magnitude –2.6. Jupiter is easily distinguished because it is brilliant white. Larger telescopes will show quite a lot of detail on Jupiter's disc, particularly the dark and light bands ("belts" and "zones") and maybe the famous Great Red Spot.

Saturn's disc is a pale imitation of Jupiter's, but this planet's shining glory is the incredibly beautiful ring system that girdles its equator. The aspect of the rings changes noticeably during Saturn's near 30-year orbit around the Sun.

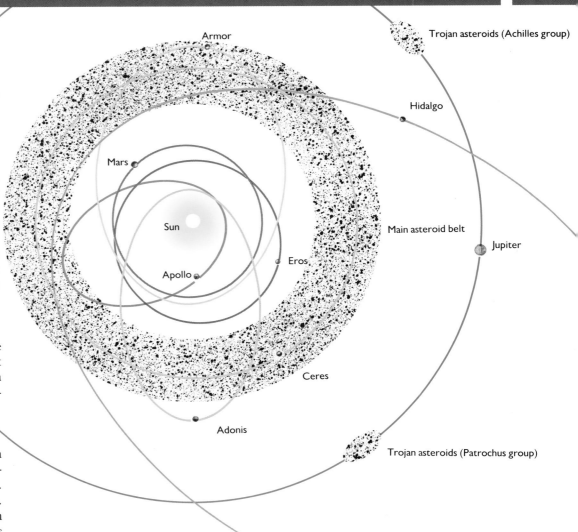

▲ The asteroid belt lies between about 275 and 550 million kilometres (170 and 340 million miles) from the Sun between the orbits of Mars and Jupiter. Some of the asteroids stray far away from the main belt, as the diagram shows. Two groups of asteroids, the Trojans, travel in the same orbit as Jupiter, locked in place by the planet's gravity.

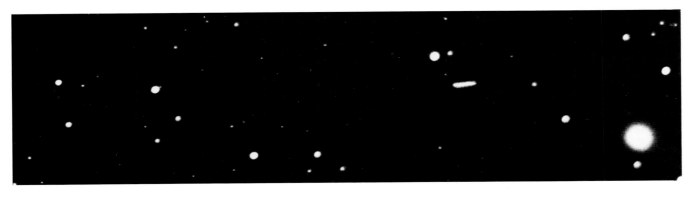

◄ Asteroids appear on long-exposure star photographs as trails because they are moving against the stellar background. In stellar photography the telescope is driven to follow the movement of the stars.

Observing Meteors and Comets

You don't have to gaze at the night sky for long before you see luminous streaks shooting across the sky. We call them meteors, or shooting stars. They are not stars, of course, but fiery trails left behind when particles from outer space burn up high in the atmosphere.

The space between the planets in the Solar System is not completely empty, but contains significant amounts of particles of rock and metal. These particles are known as meteoroids. Most are no bigger than a grain of sand, but some can be the size of large boulders.

As the Earth travels in space, it encounters meteoroid particles all the time. When they get near the Earth, they are attracted to it by gravity. They plunge into the upper atmosphere at speeds of up to 70 kilometres (43 miles) a second. Friction with the air particles generates enough heat to make them glow white-hot and eventually burn up. They leave behind the fiery trail of glowing gases we see as a meteor.

Fireballs and meteorites

Sometimes an exceptionally big meteoroid smashes into the atmosphere. It appears in the night sky as a great ball of fire we call a fireball, or bolide. If the meteoroid causing the fireball is big enough, it may survive to reach the ground, as a meteorite. It may even gouge out a crater.

Two basic types of meteorite are found, stony and iron. The stony ones are made up mainly of silicates, like many stones on Earth. The iron ones are made up of a mixture of iron and nickel, sometimes with a little cobalt.

At certain times of the year the number of meteors increases dramatically from one about every 10 minutes to maybe one or more a minute. This happens during so-called meteor showers. They occur when the Earth passes through trails of dust left behind by passing comets (*see below*).

All the meteors appear to come from one point in the sky, called the radiant. The showers are named after the constellation containing the radiant. One of the most reliable showers, the Perseids, takes place in August each year. The Leonids (November) and the Geminids (December) can also be impressive.

Comets

Comets appear less often in our skies, but can become the most spectacular of heavenly objects. The majority appear without warning, travelling into the inner reaches of the Solar System from a "reservoir" (the Oort Cloud) far beyond the orbits of the planets. Some comets, called the periodic comets, reappear regularly in the Earth's skies, travelling to and fro in known orbits. The best-known of them all, Halley's Comet, returns about every 75 years. The comet with the shortest period is Encke's Comet, which takes only 3.3 years to orbit the Sun.

Comets are lumps of ice and dust, normally frozen solid. Typically they are a few tens of kilometres across. For most of the time they remain remote and invisible.

▲ A fireball leaves a fiery trail as it streaks through the night sky. Objects producing fireballs may be large enough to reach the ground as meteorites.

▼ Meteor Crater in Arizona is remarkably well preserved, as this picture testifies. It measures 1,265 metres (4,150 feet) across and is 175 metres (575 feet) deep.

◄ Halley's Comet, pictured against a starry backcloth, on April 9 1986, on its last return to Earth's skies. It will not return again until 2061.

► Comet Ikeya-Seki (1965), visible in broad daylight in some parts of the world, was one of the brightest comets of this century.

▼ On the night of March 13/14 1986, the European space probe Giotto returned this image as it homed in on Halley's Comet. The nucleus, the darker region at top left, appears to be about 15 kilometres (9 miles) long and about 8 kilometres (5 miles) across.

Only when they travel into the inner Solar System do they make their presence known. The Sun's heat begins to evaporate some of the ice, which releases some dust. This vapour and dust cloud reflects sunlight, so the comet becomes visible. The "pressure" of the solar wind "blows" the gas and dust cloud away from the head of the comet to form a tail, which can stretch for millions of kilometres.

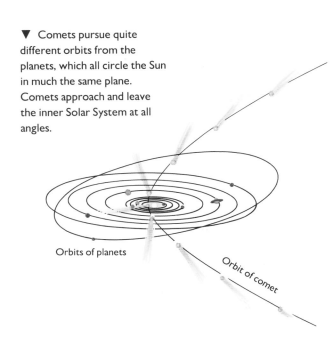

▼ Comets pursue quite different orbits from the planets, which all circle the Sun in much the same plane. Comets approach and leave the inner Solar System at all angles.

Orbits of planets

Orbit of comet

► The surface of Mercury is heavily cratered and bears more than a passing resemblance to that of the Moon. The craters are similar to Moon craters, many of them having the typical central mountain peak. Note the prominent fault line, or scarp, near the limb.

▼ This oblique relief view (with false colour) of the surface of Venus was computer-generated from data returned by the Magellan space probe. The probe, launched in May 1989, mapped virtually the whole planet over a four-year period. It found hundreds of volcanoes, with evidence of extensive lava flows, and spider-like formations called arachnoids, which are unique to Venus.

EARTH-LIKE PLANETS

The three planets that lie relatively close to Earth in the inner reaches of the Solar System are quite different from the ones that lie much farther out.

These planets, Mercury, Venus and Mars, are relatively small and made up mainly of rock, like the Earth, which is why they are often called the terrestrial planets. They contrast markedly with the outer planets, which are giant gas balls.

Mercury

Second smallest of the planets after Pluto, Mercury (diameter 4,878 kilometres, 3,031 miles) is the one closest to the Sun. It rotates slowly, taking 59 days to spin round once, while it circles the Sun every 88 days.

This slow rotation results in a point on the surface facing the Sun for periods of three months at a time. Then, surface temperatures rise as high as 425°C (800°F), which is hot enough to melt lead. On the other hand, a point on the opposite side of Mercury receives no sunshine at all for three months, and there temperatures can fall to −170°C (−275°F).

Mercury is little bigger than the Moon and likewise has no atmosphere. Its surface is also covered with craters. Unlike the Moon, however, Mercury has no large seas, or maria. Its most distinctive large surface feature is the ring-shaped Caloris Basin, which measures about 1,400 kilometres (870 miles) across.

Venus

Only marginally smaller than the Earth, Venus (diameter 12,104 kilometres, 7,521 miles) takes about 225 days to circle the Sun. It takes even longer, 243 days, to spin once on its axis. It also spins round in the opposite direction from all the other planets.

Although a near-twin of the Earth in size, Venus could hardly be more different in other respects. It has a heavy atmosphere, consisting mainly of carbon dioxide at a crushing pressure 90 times the atmospheric pressure on Earth. A runaway "greenhouse effect" has raised temperatures at the surface to 475°C (890°F) or more.

Thick clouds in the atmosphere, some formed of sulphuric acid droplets, keep the surface of Venus permanently hidden from view. We can "see" the surface only by radar. Radar scans have revealed that most of the planet consists of rolling plains. There are just two highland regions – Aphrodite Terra, which is about the size of Africa, and Ishtar Terra, which is smaller.

Mars, the Red Planet

Although it is much smaller, Mars (diameter 6,794 kilometres, 4,222 miles) resembles the Earth in a number of ways. It spins on its axis in about the same time; it has seasons; it has a slight atmosphere; and it has polar ice caps, which advance and retreat in turn in winter and summer. Because of such similarities, people once thought that Mars might harbour life, even intelligent life. But investigations by space probes such as Viking have ruled this out.

Mars takes about 687 days to circle the Sun. It is a much colder world than the Earth, with temperatures struggling to reach freezing point even at the equator in summer. In winter, temperatures can drop to $-140°C$ ($-220°F$). Carbon dioxide is the main gas in the very thin atmosphere, which has only one-hundredth the pressure of Earth's atmosphere.

Although there is no running water on Mars, there is water ice at the poles and traces of moisture in the atmosphere. This leads to clouds, mist and frost occurring in places at times.

Parts of Mars are quite heavily cratered, but its most prominent features include a huge canyon and four massive volcanoes. The Martian "Grand Canyon", Valles Marineris (Mariner Valley), runs for nearly 5,000 kilometres (3,000 miles) near the Martian equator and averages more than 100 kilometres (60 miles) across. Mariner Valley is not far from the four prominent volcanoes. The highest is the 25-kilometre (15-mile) high Olympus Mons.

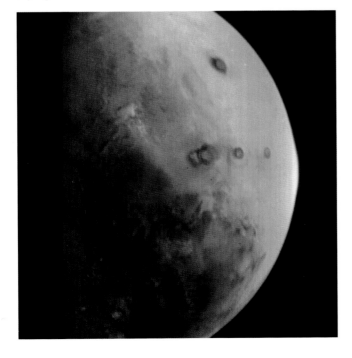

▲ The crater complex at the summit of Olympus Mons, a huge extinct volcano on Mars .

◄ This Viking approach picture shows several of Mars's outstanding features. The line of circles near the centre show the high volcanoes on the Tharsis Ridge. Above them is the massive crater of Olympus Mons. At the bottom of the picture is the circular Argyre Basin, filled with frost.

▶ Rust-red rocks are strewn across the Martian plain of Chryse, landing site of the first Viking lander in 1976.

THE GIANT PLANETS

The terrestrial planets are midgets compared with the four giant planets that lie in the outer reaches of the Solar System. In order of increasing distance from the Sun, they are Jupiter, Saturn, Uranus and Neptune.

With a diameter 11 times that of Earth, Jupiter is the giant among giants and has a greater mass than all the other planets put together! Yet even it is a dwarf compared with the Sun.

Of the four giants, only Jupiter and Saturn were known to ancient astronomers. The other two are too faint to be seen except in telescopes. William Herschel discovered Uranus in 1781, while Johann Galle discovered Neptune in 1846.

Thanks to NASA space probes, particularly the two Voyagers, all four giants are now as familiar to us as the four terrestrial planets. The giant planets differ markedly from the Earth-like inner planets in composition. They are made up mainly of the two gases, hydrogen and helium. They all have deep atmospheres, and deep oceans of liquid gas underneath. Only at their centres might there be a rocky core.

Jupiter

The light and dark belts and zones we see on Jupiter (diameter 142,800 kilometres, 88,700 miles) through a telescope are bands of clouds drawn out parallel by the planet's swift rotation – it spins round once in under 10 hours. Jupiter takes nearly 12 years to make one orbit of the Sun.

Jupiter's disc is brilliantly coloured red and orange. The furious rotation of the atmosphere sets up turbulence, particularly in the region of the huge storm centre we know as the Great Red Spot, which measures some 28,000 kilometres (17,000 miles) across.

Saturn

The second largest planet, Saturn (diameter 120,000 kilometres, 74,600 miles) is also the least dense. With a relative density of less than 1, it would, if it could, float in water. Saturn's disc is less obviously banded than Jupiter's, though winds on the planet blow more strongly – up to 1,800 km/h (1,100 mph). Saturn circles the Sun once every 29½ years.

The glorious ring system around Saturn's equator spans more than twice the planet's diameter, but is at most only about 1 kilometre (0.6 mile) thick. From Earth only three main rings are readily visible: A, B and C. Space probes have found several more and have discovered that they are made up of thousands of individual ringlets. These mark the paths of swift-moving rock and ice particles.

Uranus and Neptune

These two planets are near-twins in size; Uranus (diameter 51,200 kilometres, 31,800 miles) is about 1,600 kilometres (1,000 miles) bigger across than Neptune. At present, Neptune is the most distant of the planets because Pluto, usually the most distant, is travelling inside Neptune's orbit (until 1999). Uranus takes just slightly over 84 years to complete one orbit of the Sun, while Neptune takes almost twice as long – nearly 165 years.

The most unusual feature of Uranus is that its axis is tilted at an angle of 98° – more than a right-angle – with respect to the plane of its orbit. In effect the planet travels on its side as it orbits the Sun.

The disc of Uranus is a bluish green colour and shows virtually no features. The disc of Neptune is deep blue, and is flecked with wisps of white clouds, particularly around the dark spots, which are storm centres. Voyager 2 spotted faint rings around both Uranus and Neptune.

▼ Colourful clouds are drawn into parallel bands by the swift rotation of Jupiter's atmosphere. Here, in the south equatorial belt, the clouds eddy furiously around the Great Red Spot.

◀ This is the view you would see if you were orbiting Uranus's moon Miranda. The blue-green coloured planet is about 130,000 kilometres (81,000 miles) distant. Below, Miranda's contorted surface is geologically the most baffling in the whole Solar System.

▼ Visually, Neptune is much more interesting than Uranus. It has a surprising amount of "weather" for a planet so far from the Sun. It features stormy spots and banks of clouds. Of particular interest is the Great Dark Spot shown in the picture, a massive storm centre analogous to Jupiter's Great Red Spot.

▲ A beautiful Voyager picture of the ringed planet Saturn. It shows clearly two of the three main rings: A (outer) and B, separated by the Cassini Division. The bands of clouds in the atmosphere are less prominent than Jupiter's.

▼ Saturn's extensive ring system, compared in size with the Earth. In all, it measures some 270,000 kilometres (170,000 miles) across. The different colours in this false-colour image of the rings indicate mainly different sizes of ringlet particles.

▲ A close-up of Ganymede's surface. The white spots are fresh craters, made by impacts with rocky debris. The impacts have gouged out holes and exposed fresh ice. The curious grooved terrain shows where the crust has fractured.

▼ A volcano erupting on the limb of Io. It is spewing out molten sulphur rather than lava, which accounts for the vivid yellow-orange colour of the surface. Gas and dust are being blasted to heights of 200 kilometres (125 miles) or more.

▲ The largest moons in the Solar System compared in size. With the exception of Titan, all the moons in the outer circle belong to Jupiter. Titan is one of Saturn's moons. Ganymede (5,275 kilometres, 3,278 miles) is the largest moon, followed in turn by Titan (5,150 kilometres, 3,200 miles), Callisto (4,820 kilometres, 2,995 miles), Io (3,632 kilometres, 2,257 miles), the Moon (3,476 kilometres, 2,160 miles) and Europa (3,126 kilometres, 1,942 miles).

MANY MOONS

All the planets except Mercury and Venus have one or more satellites, or moons, orbiting around them. These bodies range in size from irregular lumps of rock tens of kilometres across to bodies bigger than Mercury.

The Earth, of course, has just one moon – the Moon. Pluto also has only one moon, Charon, which, amazingly, is half its size, with a diameter of about 1,190 kilometres (740 miles). Mars has two tiny moons – Phobos (about 28 kilometres, 17 miles across) and the slightly smaller Deimos. It is almost certain that these two rocky bodies are asteroids captured from the nearby asteroid belt.

The giant planets have an astonishing number of moons between them – more than 60! They are made up mainly of ice and rock. The Voyager probes discovered many small new moons when they flew past the planets in the 1970s and 1980s.

Jupiter has at least 16 moons, the four largest being the Galilean moons, which we can see in binoculars – Io, Europa, Ganymede and Callisto. Of these, the most interesting is Io, the only body we know, apart from the Earth, that has active volcanoes.

◄ Fault lines and craters scar the icy surface of Saturn's moon Enceladus (500 kilometres, 300 miles in diameter). This moon is one of the most reflective bodies in the Solar System: it reflects light even better than fresh snow!

The ringed planet Saturn has even more moons than Jupiter – at least 22. The largest is Titan, unique among moons because it has a thick atmosphere of nitrogen and methane. It may have methane lakes on its surface. Among the new moons discovered by the Voyager probes are so-called "shepherd" moons. They orbit near the rings and their gravity helps to keep the ring particles in place.

We can see only five of Uranus's 15 or so moons through a telescope. Of these, Miranda (diameter 485 kilometres, 300 miles) has the most extraordinary surface, which is a patchwork of different geological features, with sharp boundaries between them. For example, rolling plains suddenly give way to mysterious grooved regions. This seems to suggest that long ago Miranda collided with a large asteroid and was shattered to pieces. Then the pieces recombined under gravity to create the weird landscape we now see.

We can see only two of Neptune's eight or more moons from Earth – Triton and Nereid. Triton (diameter about 2,700 kilometres, 1,680 miles) was photographed closely by Voyager 2 and proved to be a pinkish world, peppered by icy "geysers". It is the coldest place we know in the Solar System, with a temperature of −236°C (−393°F).

▲ Two of the tiny new moons of Uranus discovered by Voyager 2 in 1986. They are "shepherd" moons on either side of the epsilon ring, helping to keep the ring particles in place.

◄ Close-up of the southern hemisphere of Neptune's moon Triton. It has a polar cap of pinkish snow, probably made up of frozen methane and nitrogen gases. The dark plumes are probably material thrown out by erupting volcanoes or geysers.

◄ Telescope domes at the Roque de Los Muchachos Observatory on La Palma in the Canary Islands. The telescopes are, from the left, the William Herschel, the Isaac Newton and the Jacobus Kapteyn. The Observatory occupies a superb mountain-top site at an altitude of some 2,400 metres (7,900 feet).

ASTRONOMERS AT WORK

When darkness falls and most of the working population head for home, supper and bed, astronomers open up the domes of their telescopes and train them on distant worlds in the unfathomable depths of space. Perhaps tonight they will search for that elusive tenth planet which some astronomers are convinced lies beyond Pluto. Or they will chart the course of a maverick, long-tailed comet. Or if they are very lucky, they will chance upon one of the most spectacular and most cataclysmic events in the Universe, a supernova.

Amateurs, too, though they have more modest instruments, still help push back the frontiers of astronomy. The Universe is a big place, and even the professionals can examine only small bits of it at any time. The huge army of amateurs dotted around the world, who each night keep sky-watch, perform inestimable service in recording the vagaries of variable stars, discovering comets newly emerged from the Stygian gloom of the outer Solar System, and spotting outbursts by novae and occasionally supernovae.

Astronomy, as the T-shirt slogan goes, is looking up.

OBSERVING THE HEAVENS

High up on mountaintops – and in suburban gardens – astronomers pursue their career or hobby that takes them, in the mind at least, out of this world.

▼ Telescope domes at Kitt Peak National Observatory, near Tucson, in Arizona. The dome on the right houses the Mayall 4-metre (157-inch) reflector, the largest instrument on site. Kitt Peak is one of the world's finest observatories, located in the Quinlan Mountains on a peak 2,095 metres (6,875 feet) above the Sonora Desert. The local Papago Indians call Kitt Peak astronomers the People with the Long Eyes.

Professional astronomers carry out their telescopic observations at observatories, which usually house a variety of instruments. Most leading observatories are located at high altitude on mountaintops in dry climates. There they are above the thickest part of the atmosphere, which is laden with dust and water vapour and prone to distorting air currents.

Kitt Peak *(below)* is a fine example, being located on a mountaintop in an arid desert region. Two of the finest observatories in the Southern Hemisphere are located within about 120 kilometres (75 miles) of each other in the foothills of the Andes in the Atacama Desert, where in some parts rain has not fallen for centuries! They are the Cerro Tololo Inter-American Observatory, which has a 4-metre (157-inch) reflector, and the European Southern Observatory, which has two 3.6-metre (141-inch) reflectors.

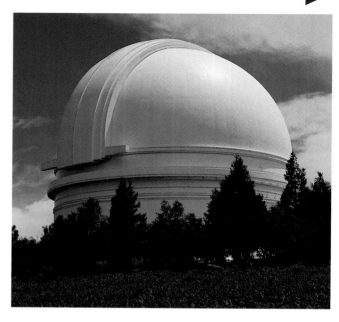

▲ The dome on Palomar Mountain, California, that houses the Hale 5-metre (200-inch) reflector, completed in 1948. Astronomers working with the new telescope, such as Edwin Hubble, pushed back the frontiers of astronomy as never before.

◀ Stonehenge on Salisbury Plain probably functioned as an astronomical observatory 4,000 years ago. This picture shows part of the outer ring of "sarsens", lined up with the distant "heel" stone.

▲ The scattered domes at the Anglo-Australian Observatory, Siding Spring, near Coonabarabran in New South Wales, Australia. The dome on the right houses the 3.9-metre (154-inch) Anglo-Australian Telescope, one of the most powerful instruments in the Southern Hemisphere.

▼ This tall tower is one of the solar telescopes at Mount Wilson Observatory, near Los Angeles, California. The Observatory is also the home of the 2.5-metre (100-inch) Hooker telescope, which first revealed the presence of external galaxies.

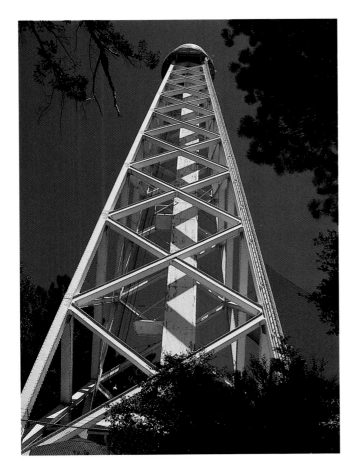

The best-known telescope, however, is the original giant, the 5-metre (200-inch) Hale Telescope at Palomar Observatory near Los Angeles. Alas, this historic giant is now suffering badly from something that is beginning to affect astronomers increasingly – light pollution.

Such large instruments are prodigious light-gatherers. It is said they are able to detect the light from a candle tens of thousands of kilometres away! But no one looks through them any more. They are used as massive cameras to record images on photographic film. Film in effect stores the light falling on it and in this way is able to detect very faint stars and galaxies.

Amateur astronomers on the other hand invariably do look through their telescopes, and some build observatories to house them. A simple design for an observatory is the so-called run-off shed. This is essentially a small shed split into two sections that can be moved apart when the telescope is required. However, it offers the observer no protection from the elements.

Such protection is essential when observing, by its nature a fairly static occupation. So wrap up well. In winter, thick sweater, padded anorak, two pairs of socks, thick boots and a woollen hat are to be recommended. So are a flask of hot tea or coffee and a snack!

Among the other equipment you will need is a torch fitted with a red bulb or filter so that it gives out a dim red light. Red light affects your night vision the least. You will need a torch to look at your equipment and another essential item, a good star map.

For your own records, if not for posterity, you should make notes on your observations on a pad, recording:
(1) The date and the time – use the 24-hour clock and follow Universal Time (Greenwich Mean Time), which means allowing for summer time when it is in force
(2) The "seeing", or viewing conditions, using the Antoniadi scale of I (ideal viewing conditions) to V (very poor conditions)
(3) Details of the telescope or binoculars used, the aperture and the magnification.

▲ America's Stonehenge, located near Salisbury, New Hampshire, also has alignments that mark the positions of the rising and setting Sun over the seasons as they would have been in about 1500 BC.

◄ Photographing circular star trails could not be simpler. Fix your camera on a tripod, point it in the direction of the celestial pole, open the shutter on the "B" setting (time exposure), and let the Earth rotate!

► You can take interesting star-trail pictures by pointing the camera at the horizon. Long-exposure photographs will then show up not only the star trails but also a silhouette of the skyline.

► (*Bottom*) To photograph the stars as points rather than trails, you need a motor drive to move the telescope/camera to follow the rotation of the heavens. This picture of the Pleiades was captured with a five-minute exposure on Tri-X film.

▲ For photographing solar eclipses, as here in Hawaii at the July 1991 eclipse, ordinary cameras are fine. But you must fit a mylar aluminized filter to photograph the partial phases. The filter cuts out most of the Sun's otherwise blinding light. You remove the filter during totality, but must put it in place immediately after photographing the "diamond ring".

PHOTOGRAPHING THE HEAVENS

If you have a camera, you can photograph the night sky and begin astrophotography. Even with the simplest equipment, you can snap the Moon, stars, planets, meteors, asteroids, comets and eclipses.

Astrophotography combines what are almost certainly the two most widely practised hobbies in the world – astronomy and photography. Once you have taken your first spools of night-sky pictures, you are likely to become addicted – as long as you do not expect at first to capture the superb colour images that adorn the covers of astronomy magazines.

▲ Copernicus and its surroundings, photographed through a telescope. However, you can take good photographs of the Moon with a tripod-mounted camera and telephoto lens.

▼ An attractive pair of nebulae to photograph using a driven telescope: M16 (left) in Serpens Cauda and M17 in Sagittarius, both about the seventh magnitude.

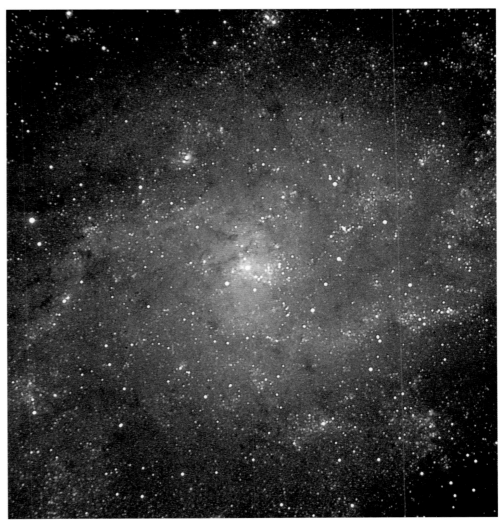

▲ The nearby galaxy M33 in Triangulum is worth studying with driven telescope and camera. Photographs will begin to reveal its wide-open spiral structure. M33 is just on the limit of naked-eye visibility. It lies at about the same distance as the Great Spiral in Andromeda, and is located quite near it in the sky.

Volumes have been written about astrophotography, and you are advised to read one if you want to take it up seriously. Here we deal with a few basics that will help get you started. The first essential is a camera with a facility for time exposure (often called a "B" setting). This is because the light from the stars is feeble, and the shutter needs to be left open for a while so that the film can "store" the light that falls upon it. You will not, however, need a time exposure for the Moon, because it is so bright.

The second essential is a sturdy tripod. This is needed to hold the camera absolutely rigid during the time exposure. If the camera wobbles, you will get a blurred image. Hanging extra weights on the tripod is always a good idea.

A wide selection of photographic films with different speeds is available. If you want to record stars as points in your pictures, you must use a fast film. This is because in less than half a minute, the stars will start to "trail" because of the rotation of the sky.

Good results can be obtained using fast film with an ISO (ASA) rating of 400, especially when it is "pushed", or developed as if it were a much faster film. Very fast films indeed are now available, with ISO (ASA) ratings of 1600 or more, although they tend to produce pictures that are "grainy". If you want simply to produce star trails, you can use much slower films (ISO 100 and 200), and you will be rewarded by finer detail and better colour.

To improve your stellar photography further, you need to drive your camera to follow the rotation of the heavens. This will enable you to take long time exposures, which will begin to record the splendour of deep sky objects, such as nebulae, clusters and galaxies. If you have a telescope with a motor drive, you can mount the camera on it, or you can fix the camera to the telescope and use the telescope as a supertelephoto lens.

► The salient features of a Newtonian reflector, the type most favoured by amateur astronomers. The eyepiece is on the side and at a convenient height for viewing.

Finderscope

Eyepiece

Body tube

Cradle

Polar axis

Declination axis

Counterweight

Sturdy tripod

▼ Explaining the principles of the telescope to a budding astronomer. This model is a 21-centimetre (8½-inch) Newtonian reflector. This is a good size for the dedicated star-gazer.

▼ A well-made 10-centimetre (4-inch) refractor like this can produce excellent images. Note the finderscope and the knob at the viewing end, which is used for focusing. The eyepiece is carried by a right-angled prism fitted into the eyepiece tube. This makes for more comfortable viewing when studying stars at high elevations.

TELESCOPES

We can see much in the night sky just with the naked eye, but to appreciate its splendour fully we need to use binoculars or a telescope. These instruments have many times the light-gathering power of the eye.

There are two main kinds of telescopes – refractors and reflectors. Both produce an upside-down image, but this does not matter for astronomical work.

Refractors use glass lenses to gather and focus starlight. They have at the far end an objective lens, or object glass. This gathers the starlight and brings it to a focus. The image is then viewed and magnified by an eyepiece lens. Binoculars are in effect a pair of refractors, one for each eye.

Reflectors use mirrors to gather starlight. There are a number of different types. The one favoured by most amateurs is the Newtonian, named after Isaac Newton, who built the first reflector in about 1668. It has a curved primary mirror, which gathers the light and reflects it on to a plane (flat) secondary mirror, which in turn reflects it into an eyepiece. The eyepiece is located near the top of the telescope tube.

The Cassegrain is another type of reflector. The light gathered by the curved primary mirror is reflected by a

▲ Polishing the 4.2-metre (165-inch) mirror of the William Herschel Telescope, now installed at the Roque de los Muchachos Observatory on La Palma, in the Canary Islands. It is one of the world's finest telescopes.

▼ The Anglo-Australian Telescope at Siding Spring, New South Wales, which has a 3.9-metre (154-inch) mirror. The open body tube is mounted inside a huge "horseshoe" bearing. The prime-focus cage is positioned nearly 13 metres (43 feet) above the mirror.

curved secondary mirror back through a hole in the primary and viewed there by an eyepiece.

Choosing binoculars

Binoculars are described by their power of magnification and the aperture, or diameter of their object glass in millimetres. Useful sizes for ordinary astronomical viewing are 8 × 40, 7 × 50 and 10 × 50. 10 × 50s are quite bulky to hand-hold steadily, and are best mounted on a tripod for observing. So must binoculars of higher magnification and aperture to prevent image-shake.

Choosing a telescope

There are good telescopes and there are cheap telescopes; there are few, if any, good cheap telescopes! The cheaper the telescope, the poorer its optics, and the poorer the image. Before you buy, you would be well advised to seek advice from an experienced star-gazer in one of the many astronomical societies found up and down the country.

About the smallest useful size for an astronomical refractor is about 60–75 millimetres (2½–3 inches) aperture, or about double this for a reflector. Refractors are in general more robust than reflectors and need less attention, but are comparatively expensive.

However good the optics of your telescope, you will get nothing but poor images if it is badly mounted. Most telescopes are mounted on a tripod, and this must be solidly made so that it stays absolutely firm when you are focusing or rotating the telescope.

The way the telescope is mounted on the tripod or other support is also important. The simplest mounting is the altazimuth. This allows you to angle the telescope up and down and also horizontally. But this mounting makes it awkward to follow the path of the stars, which travel neither vertically nor horizontally.

The best mounting is the equatorial. This allows the telescope to move around an axis (the polar axis) which is parallel with the Earth's axis and points towards the celestial pole. The path of the stars, which circle around the celestial pole, can then be followed simply by rotating the telescope around the polar axis.

▲ The 1-metre (39-inch) Jacobus Kapteyn reflector at the Roque de los Muchachos Observatory on La Palma, in the Canary Islands.

▼ The CCD (charge-coupled device) is revolutionizing optical astronomy. It is very much more sensitive to light than photographic film.

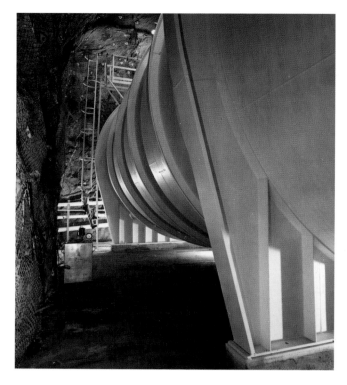

RADIO AND SPACE TELESCOPES

▲ The Arecibo radio telescope in Puerto Rico, the biggest in the world, consists of a dish 305 metres (1,000 feet) across. The dish is made of 38,778 perforated aluminium panels, suspended in a natural bowl in a mountain-top. It collects radio waves from the heavens and focuses them on the antenna suspended high above.

▲ (*Right*) This huge tank of dry cleaning fluid deep in a mine in South Dakota, USA, must be the oddest astronomical "instrument". It acts as a detector for neutrinos, which are produced in the heart of the Sun.

▶ The largest radio telescope of the Australian National Radio Observatory at Parkes, New South Wales, has a dish 64 metres (210 feet) across.

Some of the most dramatic astronomical discoveries of recent years, such as quasars and pulsars, have been made by using radio telescopes to study the radio waves stars and galaxies give out. Telescopes sent into space to pick up both visible and invisible wavelengths have also made exciting new discoveries: of stars being born, of other solar systems, and of possible black holes.

Stars give out their energy not only as visible light rays, but also as invisible gamma rays, X-rays, ultraviolet rays, infrared rays, microwaves and radio waves. All these rays are different kinds of electromagnetic radiation which differ from one another in their wavelengths. Gamma rays have the shortest wavelengths, and radio waves the longest.

The stars do not give out energy equally at all wavelengths. For example, a star that looks dim in visible light may shine like a beacon when viewed, say, at radio wavelengths. So to get a true picture of the heavens, we must view them at all wavelengths.

The trouble is that the Earth's atmosphere blocks most invisible wavelengths. Fortunately, it does let through radio waves, which makes possible radio astronomy from the ground. This science has its origins in 1931 when Karl Jansky, a Bell Telephone Laboratories researcher in the United States, discovered radio waves coming from the heavens. But radio astronomy did not really take off until after the construction of giant radio telescopes, such as the 76-metre (250-foot) dish at Jodrell Bank near Manchester, England, which was completed in 1957.

The Parkes radio telescope in Australia (left) is another powerful instrument. The dish gathers radio waves from the heavens and concentrates them on the antenna above. The signals are then fed through electronic circuits to a computer, which can display a visible image of the radio source (see page 154).

Space telescopes

The atmosphere blocks the gamma rays, X-rays, ultraviolet rays and infrared rays that reach the Earth from the stars. So astronomers have to send instruments into space on satellites to detect them. The results have been spectacular and have given astronomers quite a different view of the Universe.

Among the most outstanding satellites have been the X-ray satellites Einstein and Exosat, IUE (International Ultraviolet Explorer), IRAS (Infrared Astronomy Satellite) and the Compton (Gamma Ray) Observatory.

Optical telescopes too are carried into orbit, where they can take advantage of a position above the Earth's obscuring atmosphere. The space shuttle regularly carries astronomy payloads, as does the Russian space station Mir. But the outstanding instrument is the Hubble Space Telescope, which is producing good images despite a manufacturing fault.

▲ The telescope cluster on Astro-1, an astronomy payload carried into space in December 1990 by space shuttle Columbia. It looked at the Universe at ultraviolet wavelengths, which do not reach Earth because they are absorbed by the atmosphere.

▶ (*Top*) Two Voyager probes of this design, launched in 1977, have revolutionized the study of the outer planets. Their instruments include cameras, radiometers and particle detectors. For scale: the dish antenna measures 3.7 metres (144 inches) across.

▶ The Hubble Space Telescope, pictured in orbit. This 11-tonne (12-ton) satellite, which operates at optical wavelengths, has a mirror 2.4 metres (95 inches) across. Despite faulty optics, it has been returning better images than Earth-bound telescopes.

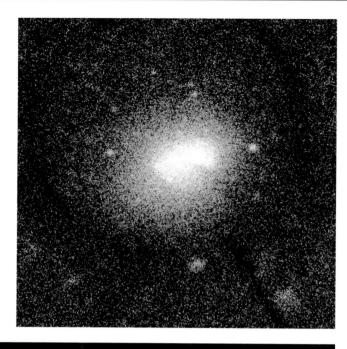

INVISIBLE IMAGES

► X-ray
An image of the cluster of galaxies called Abell 2256, returned by the German X-ray satellite Rosat (Roentgen satellite).

▼ Ultraviolet
The ultraviolet imaging telescope of the shuttle-borne satellite Astro-1 returned this image of the face-on spiral galaxy M74 in Pisces. The bright points highlight regions of intense star formation.

Most of the pictures in this book are photographs of the heavenly bodies taken with ordinary light, that is, at visible wavelengths. They show the bodies as we would see them with our eyes. The images on these pages, however, are pictures taken at invisible wavelengths. They show what we would see if our eyes were sensitive to these wavelengths.

The images have been produced from the signals picked up by detectors sensitive to the particular wavelengths under study. Computers have processed the signals and arbitrarily assigned different colours to different intensities of radiation. This results in so-called false-colour images.

The images have been selected so that they cover different wavelengths of the electromagnetic spectrum, from the short-wavelength gamma rays to the long-wavelength radio waves.

▼ Infrared
Comet IRAS-Araki-Alcock of 1983, first detected by IRAS (infrared astronomy satellite). During its 300-day mission, IRAS also peered into the centre of our Galaxy; spotted stars being born in nebulae; and detected discs of matter around other stars, which may eventually condense into planets.

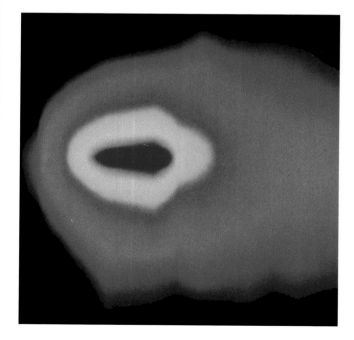

▶ Microwave

A microwave map of the whole sky, produced from data returned by COBE (cosmic background explorer). The colour differences reflect very slight variations in the background temperature, which averages about three degrees above absolute zero. Such variations are predicted by the Big Bang theory of the creation of the Universe.

▼ Microwave radar

The planet Venus, as we could never see it in visible light. This global view is a mosaic of images obtained by radar scans by the orbiting Magellan space probe in 1990/91.

▼ Radio

A false-colour image of the radio source 3C75 in the Abell 400 cluster of galaxies in Cetus. NRAO's Very Large Array radio telescope near Socorro, New Mexico, gathered the data using its 27 antennae. The image shows twin radio "jets" coming from the nucleus of the central galaxy in the cluster.

GLOSSARY

Absolute magnitude   A measure of the true brightness of a star. It is what the brightness of the star would be if viewed from a distance of 10 parsecs, or 32.6 light years.

Active galaxy   One that has an exceptionally high energy output.

Antoniadi scale   A scale used by an observer to indicate the quality of seeing.
I   Perfect seeing
II   Mainly calm, but slight disturbance
III Moderate seeing, more disturbance
IV   Poor seeing, constant disturbance
V   Very bad seeing, very bad disturbance

Apparent magnitude   A measure of the brightness of a star as we see it from Earth.

Asteroids   Small rocky bodies that circle the Sun, mainly in a "belt" between the orbits of Mars and Jupiter. Also called the minor planets and planetoids.

Astrology   Study of the positions of the heavenly bodies with a view to explaining events in people's lives or foretelling the future.

Astronomical unit (AU)   The distance between the Earth and the Sun, 149,600,000 kilometres (93,000,000 miles).

Astronomy   The scientific study of the Universe and the bodies therein – the Sun, the Moon, the planets, their moons, the stars and the galaxies.

Aurora   A colourful glow seen mainly in far northern and far southern skies, produced when charged particles from the Sun collide with particles in the upper atmosphere. In northern skies it is called the aurora borealis, or Northern Lights; and in southern skies the aurora australis, or Southern Lights.

Big Bang   The name for the event that is believed to have created the Universe, some 15,000 million years ago.

Binary   A two-star system in which the stars are associated and circle around a common centre of gravity (barycentre).

Black hole   A region of space in which gravity is so immensely strong that not even light can escape from it.

Celestial sphere   An imaginary sphere around the Earth, to the inside of which the stars seem to be fixed.

Cepheids   A common class of variable stars that vary in brightness as regularly as clockwork. They are named after the prototype star Delta Cephei.

Comet   A small member of the Solar System, a "dirty snowball" of rock, ice and dust, which starts to shine when it approaches the Sun.

Conjunction   The lining up of heavenly bodies in the sky, such as a planet, the Sun and the Earth.

Constellations   Imaginary patterns that the bright stars make in the night sky.

Cosmology   The study of the origin, evolution and structure of the Universe.

Culmination   The maximum altitude of a heavenly body above the horizon; this happens when it crosses the meridian.

Declination   A star's celestial latitude on the celestial sphere, measured in degrees north (+) or south (−) of the celestial equator.

Double star   A pair of stars that appear close together in the sky. In a binary star, the two components are physically associated. In an optical double, the components are usually quite separate, appearing together only because they lie in the same direction.

Eclipse   The passing of one heavenly body in front of another, blotting out its light. A solar eclipse, or an eclipse of the Sun, occurs on Earth when the Moon passes in front of the Sun. A lunar eclipse, or an eclipse of the Moon, occurs when the Moon moves into the Earth's shadow in space.

Eclipsing binary   A binary-star system that varies in brightness when its two components periodically pass in front of one another in our line of sight.

Ecliptic   The apparent path of the Sun through the heavens during the year.

Elongation   The angular distance between a planet and the Sun.

Equinoxes   Times of the year when the lengths of the day and the night are equal all over the world because the Sun is directly over the Equator. This happens twice: on March 21 (the vernal, or spring equinox); and on September 23 (the autumnal equinox).

Evening star   A planet (usually Venus) that shines brightly in the western sky at sunset.

Expanding Universe   The theory that the Universe is getting bigger. Astronomers believe that expansion began with the Big Bang.

Fireball   An exceptionally bright meteor; also called a bolide.

Galaxy   A star "island" in space. Galaxies are usually elliptical or spiral in shape. We usually call our own galaxy, the Galaxy, or the Milky Way.

Globular cluster   A globe-shaped group of stars numbering up to a million or more.

Gravity   The force with which the Earth attracts any object near it. The other heavenly bodies exert a similar force. Gravity is the force that literally holds the Universe together.

Librations   Oscillations of the Moon as we see it from Earth that enable us to see slightly "round the edges" of the face it presents.

Light year   A common unit for measuring distances in space. It is the distance light travels in a year: 9.46 million million kilometres (5.88 million million miles).

Limb   The edge of the visible disc of a planet or a moon.

Luminosity   A measure of the total energy given off by a star.

Lunar   Relating to the Moon.

Magnitude   The scale on which star brightness is measured. On the scale, the visible stars are divided into six levels of brightness, and the scale is extended to describe brighter and dimmer stars. See also *Absolute magnitude; Apparent magnitude.*

Mare   A large plain on the Moon. "Mare" (plural "maria") is the Latin word for "sea". The dark areas we see on the moon are maria. The main sea areas (and English names) are:
Lacus Mortis (Lake of Death)
Lacus Somniorum (Lake of Dreams)
Mare Crisium (Sea of Crises)
Mare Fecunditatis (Sea of Fertility)
Mare Frigoris (Sea of Cold)
Mare Humorum (Sea of Humours)
Mare Imbrium (Sea of Showers)
Mare Nectaris (Sea of Nectar)
Mare Nubium (Sea of Clouds)
Mare Orientale (Eastern Sea)
Mare Serenitatis (Sea of Serenity)
Mare Smythii (Smyth's Sea)
Mare Tranquillitatis (Sea of Tranquillity)
Mare Vaporum (Sea of Vapours)
Oceanus Procellarum (Ocean of Storms)
Sinus Iridum (Bay of Rainbows)
Sinus Medii (Central Bay)
Sinus Roris (Bay of Dews)

Meridian The great circle on the celestial sphere that passes through the north and south poles. An observer's meridian passes through the north and south points on the horizon and the zenith.

Meteor A streak of light we see when a piece of rock from outer space plunges through the atmosphere and burns up.

Meteorite A piece of rock from outer space big enough to survive its passage through the atmosphere and reach the ground.

Milky Way A pale band of light that we can often see arching across the heavens. It is a region dense with stars and is, in effect, a cross-section of our Galaxy, which is also called the Milky Way.

Moon A natural satellite of a planet.

Morning star A planet (usually Venus) that shines brightly in the eastern sky at dawn.

Nadir The point on the celestial sphere directly beneath an observer.

Nebula A cloud of gas and dust between the stars. We see bright nebulae because they glow or reflect light; we see dark nebulae because they obscure light from distant stars.

Neutron star An incredibly dense body made up of a solid mass of neutrons. See also *Pulsar*.

Nova A "new" star; actually one that suddenly increases greatly in brightness.

Nuclear fusion The joining together of the nuclei (centres) of light atoms, such as hydrogen, to make heavier ones, such as helium. It is the energy-production process in stars.

Occultation The temporary hiding of one heavenly body by another, for example of a star or a planet by the Moon.

Open cluster A loose grouping of stars, typically containing a few hundred members.

Opposition The position of a planet in its orbit when it lies exactly opposite the Sun in the sky.

Parallax principle The apparent change in position of a nearby object against a distant background when looked at from different angles. The parallax of a star is the angle subtended at the star by the Earth's radius.

Parsec The unit professionals generally use to measure distances in space. It is the distance at which the parallax of a star would be one second of arc (1/3600th of a degree). Equal to 3.26 light years.

Phases The different shapes of the Moon we see in the sky during the month, as more or less of its surface is lit up by the Sun. Venus shows noticeable phases as well.

Planets Large bodies that circle in space around the Sun. Some of the other stars probably have planets circling around them.

Precession A slow change in the direction in which the Earth's axis points in space, which over the years alters the positions of the stars on the celestial sphere.

Proper motion Observed motion of a nearby star against the stellar background.

Pulsar A rapidly rotating neutron star that gives off pulses of radiation.

Quasar A remote body that looks like a star but has the energy output of many galaxies. Also called quasi-stellar object (QSO).

Radial motion Motion of a star towards or away from us, detectable from its spectrum.

Retrograde motion Motion of a heavenly body in the opposite direction from usual.

Right ascension A star's celestial longitude, expressed usually in hours and minutes of sidereal time. It is measured from the point (First Point in Aries) where the ecliptic meets the celestial equator at the vernal equinox.

Saros A period of a little over 18 years (6,585.3 days), after which the Moon returns to exactly the same position in relation to the Sun and the Earth. It therefore marks the interval between successive eclipses of the same type.

Satellite A small body that circles around a larger one in space; a moon. Most of the planets have natural satellites. The Earth has one, the Moon. Saturn has more than 20. Earth also now has thousands of artificial satellites circling around it, launched into orbit by space scientists.

Seasons Periods of the year marked by noticeable changes in the weather, especially in temperature. They occur because of the tilt in the Earth's axis with respect to the plane of its orbit around the Sun.

Seeing The quality of the observing conditions at the time of observation.

Sidereal time Time measured in relation to the stars, based on the sidereal day, the Earth's true period of rotation on its axis, 23 hours 56 minutes 4 seconds of ordinary clock time.

Solar System The family of the Sun that travels through space as a unit. At the centre is the Sun, around which circle nine planets (including the Earth), the asteroids and numerous comets.

Solar wind A stream of charged particles given off by the Sun.

Solstices Times of the year when the Sun reaches its highest and lowest points in the sky at noon. In the Northern Hemisphere, it reaches its highest point on about June 21 (summer solstice), and its lowest on December 21 (winter solstice). The dates are reversed in the Southern Hemisphere.

Spectrum A band of colour (spread of light wavelengths) produced when light is passed through a spectroscope. Stellar spectra are crossed by dark lines.

Speed of light Light travels in a vacuum at a speed of about 300,000 kilometres (186,000 miles) a second. It is the fastest speed possible.

Star A gaseous body that produces energy by nuclear fusion. It releases this energy as light, heat and other radiation. The Sun is our local star.

Sunspot An area on the Sun's surface that is darker and cooler than normal. Sunspots come and go regularly over a period of about 11 years.

Supernova A gigantic stellar explosion in which a supergiant star blasts itself apart.

Supernova remnant An expanding shell of gas resulting from a supernova explosion.

Terminator The boundary between the sunlit and dark halves of the Moon or a planet.

Transit The movement of one small heavenly body in front of a larger one, such as Venus across the disc of the Sun.

Universe Everything that exists: the Earth, the Moon, the Sun, the planets, the stars and even space itself.

Variable star One that changes in brightness. Intrinsic variables (such as Cepheids) vary in brightness because of internal physical changes. Extrinsic variables (such as eclipsing binaries) vary because of some external influence.

Zenith The point on the celestial sphere directly above an observer.

Zodiac An imaginary band in the heavens in which the Sun, Moon and planets are always found. It is occupied by 12 constellations, the constellations of the zodiac.

INDEX

Constellations are shown in capitals. Page numbers in bold refer to main entries. Page numbers in italics refer to illustrations or maps. Textual matter may also occur on the same pages.

Deep sky objects identified only by M or NGC numbers which appear on maps but not in the text are omitted from the index as are lunar features which appear only in the quadrants.

ACKNOWLEDGMENTS

The author and publishers would like to thank Spacecharts Photo Library for picture research and for supplying many of the photographs in the book. They are also indebted to the following establishments for providing invaluable information and illustrative material: Anglo-Australian Observatory, Astronaut Memorial Planetarium and Observatory, European Space Agency, Goddard Space Center, Jet Propulsion Laboratory, Kitt Peak National Observatory, London Planetarium (p.35), National Aeronautics and Space Administration, National Radio Astronomy Observatories, Palomar Observatory, Parkes Radio Observatory, Roque de los Muchachos Observatory, Royal Astronomical Society, Royal Greenwich Observatory, US Naval Observatory.

Photographs on the following pages were taken by the author: 6, 90, 102t, 126tr, 128, 129, 134bl, 136b, 146, 147, 148t, 150bl, 151, 152lt, 152b. The photograph on page 73 was taken by David Malin, courtesy Anglo-Australian Observatory.

While every effort has been made to trace and acknowledge all copyright holders, we would like to apologize should there have been any omissions.

The publishers would also like to thank Moira Greenhalgh for supplying the index.